C000155523

SINCE YOU WENT AWAY

Liz Astor, Lady Astor of Hever, lives in Kent with her husband Johnnie, who is the Defence Minister in the House of Lords. They have two children, Charles and Olivia, who is autistic, as well as Liz's daughter Natalya and Johnnie's three daughters from their respective previous marriages. Liz's book *Loving Olivia*, her memoir of caring for her autistic daughter, was published by Rodale in 2006. Liz is involved with several autism charities and her interests are in the arts, travel and reading. *Since You Went Away* is her first novel.

Since You Went Away

LIZ ASTOR

Argo Navis Author Services

Distributed in 2012 by
Argo Navis Author Services
Bloomsbury House,
74–77 Great Russell Street,
London WC1B 3DA

Typeset by Argo Navis Author Services

Printed in the UK by Lightning Source

A CIP record for this book
is available from the British Library

ISBN 978-1-909407-01-5

For Roger,
Diana and Charles

With eternal love and gratitude

In memory of my beloved mother

10p from the sale of this book will go to Parkinson's UK to help ensure that no-one has to face Parkinson's alone. The donation will also help fund vital research towards better treatments and a cure.

Prologue

God moves in a mysterious way
His wonders to perform
He plants his footstep in the sea,
And rides upon the storm.

William Cowper, 1731–1800

Dear Maisie,

As I told you on the phone last night, I have explained to Billy and the kids the type of work I'll be doing in Argentina through the Committee on the Elimination of Discrimination against Women {CEDAW} and I am *so* excited about it! At last I'm going to do something worthwhile in my life, perhaps even something important. *Finally* I will be able to use my Spanish for a *real purpose* and my M.A. in Latin American Politics will certainly be of use as I already know the history both political and social of the country. Being able to help poor, deprived women gain some financial independence and have somewhere to go if they have been raped or suffered physical and mental abuse will be extremely rewarding.

I expect to be away for about 6 months, a year at the most, and Billy has said he will do less touring and so be at home much more. He and the kids have been very supportive, if rather surprised, as the opportunity came rather suddenly, a bit of a bolt out of the blue for us all. Although they are not kids any more, are they? Jane is almost nineteen and Ricky will be seventeen in the spring. *I left home at seventeen, for Christ's sake!* And they still have their father to turn to if they need him, and the family home. I have always wanted to do this kind of work, but having children put an end to all my dreams, until now. I must go - *I cannot miss this chance, it means so much to me.*

BUT . . . I have *also* fallen madly, gloriously in love for the first time in my life! Fernando has been a visiting professor at the university and it was through him that I learnt about CEDAW. I know you will assume that at forty-eight I am having a mid-life crisis, but Maisie, I am *not*. This is it. This *really* is it. I have met my soul mate and I can hardly believe my good fortune. *Of course I did not tell Billy or the kids about Fernando, this is for your eyes only!* It is enough for them to know I am going for a cause, on a mission if you will, and the passion just adds so much to it, as you can imagine. Fernando is a radical Argentinean and will be a great help to me introducing me to important people, and his support will be invaluable. Don't cast me as the villain or think of me as selfish or deluded. Be happy for me that my time has come at last. You and Tommy have such a love match, don't deny me mine. I don't even know why I am telling you about Fernando, but I am so happy that I have to tell *someone!* I suppose I hope you might understand, knowing how close you are to Tommy.

But to the point. I am writing to ask you to tell Mum and Dad. And also look in occasionally on Billy, Jane and Ricky. I have given them my address which they can pass on to you.

The taxi is here!

Wish me luck!

With love as ever,

Ruth

Dear Ruth,

I hope you arrived safely and were not too tired after the journey. It is such a long way to go!

We are all fine here, or as well as can be expected after the shock of your sudden departure. I told Mum and Dad as you requested, but it was not a task I would like to repeat. Dad was very angry and did more than his usual share of ranting and raving, bringing up all the old stuff again. He will die a doggedly hard working, self-made man and nothing will change his point of view of either sociologists or left wing politics, I'm afraid. I explained that it was very common for a university professor to take a sabbatical and that was more or less what you're doing, isn't it? Anyway, I pointed out that if Billy and the children were supportive of your decision, then they should be too, and that the time will pass quickly enough.

As for your falling in love, I don't know what to say. I have always thought that you and Billy were happy together in your own way. Do you intend to leave Fernando when the time is up and return to Billy just as if nothing has happened? If so, you are made of much stronger stuff than I am, but you always were. I can't imagine living such a complicated life; the mere thought of it fills me with horror. And it makes me question your need 'to do something worthwhile with your life.' Was being a wife and mother as well as a university professor not worthwhile, or is the work for CEDAW just a ploy to be able to run away with Fernando? Needless to say, your secret is safe with me, but frankly, I would rather have not known it. It has made me feel extremely uncomfortable whenever I speak to Billy or your children, and I also find it awkward to look them straight in the eye.

We are all wondering why you haven't been in touch? Are you going to get a new email address and a mobile? We can only communicate by mail at the moment and letters take ages to arrive, about 10 days I was told at the post office, which leaves us all in rather a fix if an emergency arises. Anyway, this was just a note to say that we are all thinking of you and would very much like to hear from you.

With much love,

Maisie

Dear Ruth,

What on *earth* is going on? Are you all right? I am full of anxiety as you have already been away for two and half months and no one has had *a single word* from you for the entire time! Are you in some serious trouble? Have the police taken against your work, or some politician? Are you in prison? I am left to imagine that something has gone gravely wrong, otherwise why would you not have even contacted your own children? If I feel so concerned, I can't imagine how they must be feeling. I haven't asked them directly as I do not want to worry them even more, but they must be suffering agonies over your silence and no doubt Billy will be too. Whenever we meet I just ask, 'had any news from Mum yet?' and they shake their heads and don't say anything else, except last week Jane said to me, "well, you know Mum. Once she's in a passion about something, nothing else exists. Not even us!" She tried to laugh it off but I could see she was deeply hurt and puzzled. So come on Ruth, at least write to your *family, please.* It'll be Christmas in just over a month and surely you won't wait till then?

And do you have an email address or mobile number yet?
With love,

Maisie

Dear Ruth,

Silence. A new millennium and yet nothing *at all* from you, not even a *Christmas card to your own children.*

What the hell is going on? What in God's name do you think you are doing scribbling two lines to Billy telling him that you are never coming back and that he should get on with his own life? After more than twenty years of marriage, Billy didn't deserve to be treated so cruelly. It was unspeakably callous of you, as well as extremely selfish. For *Christ' sake,* Ruth, are you completely out of your mind? Please tell me this is not all because of a stupid teenage infatuation. That would be beyond the pale, Ruth. In case you have forgotten, you are forty-eight years old and the mother of two teenage children *as well as* a wife. I don't know what's got into you, but whatever it is, I find it detestable. The only possible explanation for your extraordinary behaviour is that you're in some serious kind of trouble, in which case please *tell us,* and we'll do everything we can to help you. Or you'd been kidnapped by a cult like Patty Hearst, or become a radical Jihadist, which seems unlikely in South America. I really don't know if I am more full of anger *with* you or more anxious *about* you, as you have already been away for four months and no one has had *a single word* from you for the entire time, apart from your brutal note to Billy.

I am really, really concerned and at a complete loss to know what to do or to say to your husband, your children and our parents. *Please, please* contact us, not for my sake, but for the sake of your own *children,* Ruth! I can't believe that you could be so heartless, so I am left to imagine that you are in some terrible trouble or difficulty.

Love,

Maisie

Ruth,

You really aren't ever coming back, are you? You've just abandoned everyone for the sake of your selfish '*love*' haven't you? You might think you can discard Billy like some unwanted old rag, but you can't divorce your own *children,* Ruth. I'm so angry with you that I wash my hands of you, unless you *finally* deign to reply with a genuinely viable reason. It is the only explanation I can think of for your relentless, heartless silence, unless, God forbid, you have been killed. But even then, I feel sure that we would have been informed by the British Embassy or CEDAW by now.

I give up.

Maisie

Ten Years Later

God is working his purpose out,
as year succeeds to year.
God is working his purpose out,
and the time is drawing near;
nearer and nearer draws the time,
the time that shall surely be,
when the earth shall be filled
with the glory of God,
as the waters cover the sea.

Arthur Ainger

Dear Ruth,

We have had no contact with you *whatsoever* since you went away
ten years ago.

I have no idea if you are even still alive, let alone where you are
living, so I am posting this letter to the only address we have ever
had, but from which you have never replied. I felt duty bound
to try to contact you once more to tell you, should you still care,
that our mother died two weeks ago.

If you receive this letter and wish to know what has happened
in the intervening years, then please reply. There is much to tell
and not all of it good news, but Mum's last words were all about
you. She spoke of you with great tenderness and understanding
and I hope that will bring you some measure of comfort.

Yours,

Maisie

Dear Maisie,

So I will never see my mother again. I knew what I was doing when I left, and I never in my *wildest dreams* thought I would still be here ten years later, but things did not go as I expected, and now it is too late.

I will begin with an apology. In the first few weeks after I left home I received several letters from you, Billy and my children, but the truth is that after reading the first few I could not bear to read any more, Maisie. I couldn't even bear to have them in the house in case I was tempted, knowing that their contents would torture me. And so I threw every single one in the bin unread, after I had torn them to shreds. And now our mother has died. Why was this particular letter the one I finally dared to open? Perhaps it was because there had been so many intervening years since anyone last wrote that I instinctively knew you must have something important to tell me, to drive you to write once more. So I picked up my silver letter opener and slit the envelope with an almost overwhelming feeling of foreboding. Maisie, I am devastated. I have wept every day since your letter arrived. It came as such a shock, you see. I know it is entirely my fault, but my God what a blow is was for me to receive. I am ashamed that I did not contact her once throughout all that time, but I stupidly and naively never expected her to die *just yet*.

You said she spoke of me at the end. What exactly did she say? Please tell me word for word if you can remember, because if they were indeed kind words as you said, I would dearly love to hear them. Whatever I said, however I behaved growing up, I really loved her, Maisie. You *must believe* me. I adored her brain, her energy and her ability to deal with people. And now I can never tell her myself, or explain why I did those things. I should have done it after I left home and became a mother myself. But I had my own problems of a different nature during those years, and it never crossed my mind.

You say that there is a lot to tell me and 'not all of it good.' I think I have been away long enough now to be able to read *it all*, although I will await your letters with fearful anticipation, if you can still find it in your heart to reply. It was only by shutting the door firmly behind me mentally and physically, and *never looking back* that made my life here possible. Do I have any regrets? Of course! I *am human*, whatever you may think! Knowing that I would still be here ten years later, which was *never* my original intention, I wonder if I would still have left, but I have paid for my fire and freedom with heavy measures of guilt, which includes Billy. However, I am no Anna Karenina. I can, and do, stand the pain. I was born a wild child, and have often thought I have a gypsy spirit like Scarlet O'Hara, and you, mild and pure of heart, were born a Melanie. We are the lion and the lamb sisters. And you found your Ashley in Tommy and I, at last, my Rhett. And when I left so suddenly, it must truly have seemed as if I had 'Gone with the Wind.' But most importantly, how are my children? I think of them *every single day* although I suspect they must hate me now.

Lovingly,

Ruth

Dear Ruth,

Thank God you are still alive! It is so long since we have seen or heard from you, I hardly know where to begin. But first let me reassure you that your children are fine, now. I rang them as soon as I received your letter to tell them that I had heard from you, but I'm sorry to have to tell you that by now too many years have passed for them to care. They were deeply hurt and affected not only by your pitiless letter to Billy, but also by your neglect and silence, particularly Ricky, so their response was first surprise, and then downright dismissive. I'm afraid that they are equally categorical in their refusal to write to you; although I tried my best to persuade them to do so, but I'm sure their reaction cannot come as a surprise under the circumstances. To tell you everything that has happened over the last ten years is a tall order, as naturally, much has taken place.

I'm sorry that news of Mum's death came as such a blow to you Ruth. For us, Mike and me, it had been a long time in coming, but when the end finally arrives, no matter how prepared you think you are, it is always a shock, a hollow feeling, an emptiness, a void. And although we are all in our late middle age and have grownup children of our own, it still feels as if something primordial has been removed from our lives. As if, although the new day still dawns bright, the warmth has been taken from the sun. A mother leaves a unique, irreplaceable hole in one's life. And now I see even in yours, Ruth. I know only too well that you and she always had a difficult relationship, but I also know that you loved each other deeply, despite your differences.

Mum was in a very bad way during her final week after a long period of slow deterioration. She was in a drug induced sleep most of the time, but the last time she came round she expressed great sadness at not seeing you again before she died. What she said was that she had always loved and understood you and wished she had been able to tell you once more, and to see that you believed her.

With love,

Maisie

P.S. By the way, I have never asked if you had any regrets! Are you enjoying your work? I would love to hear more about it. And I loved your description of us as 'the lion and the lamb sisters.' Do you think we are still? I am far less lamb like than I was, through necessity mostly.

Dear Maisie,

So my children don't want to know me any more and my mother died without a word from me. It is no more than I could have expected, as you pointed out, but the sting it gave will never leave me, like a prolonged and painful death, which I hope was not the case for our mother - because you mentioned that she had been deteriorating for a long time before she died. However, I have to thank you for replying at all, it is very noble and forgiving of you.

You say that Jane and Ricky "are fine, now." What does that mean? Please reply, and as quickly as you can, although I know I don't deserve it. But now we are in communication, I desperately want to know what happened after I left. I feel a great sense of urgency, and so if you would email me, it would be very much faster, and I promise I'll reply promptly. It seems our roles are reversed as I am entirely in your hands.

You asked about my work. Over the past ten years I have travelled a great deal around the country, setting up projects to help women, and was often in remote small towns where general living conditions were basic. The work has been both extremely rewarding and exhausting, but by its very nature, it was sometimes frightening, although not often actually dangerous. Although women are protected in many ways in this country, they are also extremely vulnerable to domestic abuse, and of course, abortion is illegal. Therefore many women have to resort to illegal abortions and they are treated very badly in hospitals where they frequently end up, haemorrhaging after a botched job. Only as recently as 1999 legislation was passed on sexual offences that introduced the *concept* of sexual abuse and a wider definition of rape. But most women find it impossible to prove a rape and live in fear of retribution, particularly from their own families, and so have no resort but to endure it. We are there to help them collect evidence and take their case to court, an enormous challenge in itself as we first have to convince these women that it is worth their while in the long run. And of course most husbands, fathers, brothers and, indeed, all male family members react in violent anger. Many, many times our tiny offices were attacked and even burnt to the ground. Threats are a daily hazard. But I am back in Buenos Aires now and expect to stay here.

My email address is: <u>ruthbraydon@cedaw.com.ar</u>. I will post this letter as I expect you will have changed your email address by now.

With love,

Ruth

From: Maisie Wilton maisiewilton@btinternet.com
Date: 5th January 2011
To: Ruth Braydon ruthbraydon@cedaw.com.ar

Dear Ruth,

Happy New Year. I hope you had a nice Christmas. We had all the family here, including your children, and it was a very happy day considering that Mum had so recently died.

I have only just received your letter. It must have been delayed in the usual Christmas postal chaos as well as the Christmas and New Year holidays. I agree it is much better to email as the post takes so long to reach you. My email address is above. But before I begin I just wanted to tell you that I was so interested to hear about your work, which raised many questions. Do you work with a doctor and a lawyer? Are you an all female team? Do the women who were abused by their husbands generally divorce them? Is divorce frowned upon in Argentina? Being a staunch Catholic country I can only assume that it is.

I will try to tell you what has happened since you left, but as you have said you want to know everything, and you have been away for ten years, I need to start at the beginning if it is to make any sense and not come out a jumbled muddle. So I'll begin with Mum, but of course the whole picture is an interwoven tapestry of our family.

She had not been well for some time, ever since she broke her hip by falling on the pavement outside Marks and Spencer, ten years ago. You had only been in Argentina a few weeks, and I did write straight away, and although I had no reply, I assumed that you had known. Now I know that you didn't open those letters, it will come as news to you. I tried to explain to Dad that you might have been sent away from Buenos Aires and so might not have received my letter, but you know what he's like, so black and white in his thinking. He has always found it difficult to appreciate someone else's point of view and there was no change that time. Poor Dad, he's not a natural carer and couldn't cope with Mum's being in need. So we all did the best we could, that is Tommy and I did, because of course Mike was in Australia and you were in South America. But that was fine; Tommy and I looked after Mum until she was over the worst. Actually, I moved in for about a month as it was easier all round but even so Dad was in a state and more feisty than usual; but we knew it was just the worry talking. Mum had always taken care of the house, the food and so on and he was at a complete loss with her being in bed and unable to do anything, even though I took over all her physical care and Tommy did the shopping and helped with the cleaning and washing when he come home from work. I can hear you snort 'and what about Dad? Did he lift a finger to help? It's about time he did something!' But a leopard never changes his spots. We are what we are, Ruth.

It was hard for Mum, the broken hip, and she never fully recovered from that fall. She was sent to Newcastle General Hospital and of course I went to visit her immediately after receiving an emergency phone call from Dad. It was New Year's Eve and a bad night all round as my car was in Mel's workshop having repairs done to the bodywork. A young girl had slid into me the day before on black ice and had done quite a substantial amount of damage, and Tommy had taken our children out in his car for a pizza and then on to the cinema. So I rang Mel to see if I could collect my car, but he had already removed the door and the side panel and was about to close and go home. He had offered to take old Mungo Doyle back with him to share his New Year's Eve dinner, and Mungo said that one good turn deserved another, and he would come and collect me immediately and drive me to hospital first. I was so relieved that I completely forgot about Mungo's car. I wonder if you remember it? A white rust bucket, semi-sheltering an abused and cranky engine that had once been a Nissan Micra. Lonely old Mungo talked all the way, often turning to look at me for what seemed like whole minutes at a time. If that wasn't bad enough, I could see his eyes had deteriorated almost as much as his car, so even when he was looking through the windscreen I can't imagine he could see very much! He drove through all the amber lights and risked several red because he knew I was "dead anxious about me Mam" and he was going to get me there with the "speed of greased lightening". By the time we arrived at the General I was shaking with nerves and suppressed giggles. Mungo hit the kerb at almost every turning on the way and particularly badly on a left hand turn, and I said 'watch out Mungo!' and 'oops!' so often that in the end I shut up, closed my eyes, and prepared to meet my maker. I know you'd ask, so I checked. He still has one hubcap remaining!

It took a while to find Mum and when I did, what a sorry state she was in! The A&E doors at the General were already splattered with blood and vomit, and it was still only 7pm! The good old northeast has not lost its zest for bringing in the New Year. Those poor nurses. Can you imagine what they had to deal with during the eternal night? When I look back at that night I shudder to think of Jane doing the same, but she seems to be thriving on it, and she is no longer at the General. Some of the kids in the waiting room looked half dead, slumped beside their gum-chewing, bedraggled girlfriends and distraught family members, all bashed up and bleeding, waiting in groaning agony for a doctor to see them. Luckily Mum had already been X-rayed and was in a ward before the worst of the New Year's Eve excesses hit the A&E, but the ward was awful too. She was in a large room with about twelve very sick old people, and the poor woman in the bed beside her was screaming her head off, bellowing for more painkillers, mad as a hatter if you ask me, and nothing would quieten her. The nurses were rushed off their feet and doing the best they could under the circumstances. Most of them were only kids like your Jane and probably wished they were out having a good time themselves rather than looking after all those complaining old people and drunken teenagers. What a nightmare.

Anyway, I did what I could for Mum, which wasn't much. I had dashed by her house and packed one of her favourite nighties, wash bag and a book, while Mungo waited outside, revving the accelerator to an ear-piercing scream because his engine kept cutting out, but when I went in the following morning she was beside herself and hadn't slept a wink all night. Apparently the mad woman continued to shout and call out throughout the entire night; she must have had dementia because her language was extremely coarse. She called those poor, hard working young nurses 'bitches' and kept shouting out "why ya bugger, the pain's killing wa" in broad Tyneside, which was only funny the first time. She was just like the woman who took the money outside the Freak Show tent at the fair on the town moor. You'll remember her, I'm sure. Enormously fat, with huge hairy arms like Desperate Dan's folded beneath her vast bosom, which as a child, I was sure were cows' udders, not breasts at all, with a roll-up

23

hanging from the corner of her mouth and one of the loudest voices at The Hoppings. A Beryl Cook character, without the humour. Anyway, the mad woman in the ward was also a racist and when a Jamaican nurse came to help her, she shouted out "she wasna ganna to be touched by nay stinking darkie" and so she was left to suffer all night, but of course everyone else in the ward was forced to endure her shouting.

Mum said that wasn't even half of it either, because from seven o'clock in the morning until ten at night the television blasted out one dreadful soap after another at maximum volume until she was nearly driven crazy by the noise, let alone the content. "It's like Chinese water torture, except with sound," she said. You know what I mean, where the victim is forced to lie on his back and water is dripped onto the middle of his forehead, for days on end. At least that's what Tommy told me. He said he'd read about it in a book. Well, I made as much fuss as I dared and as politely as I could, without raising anyone's ire, and by lunchtime had succeeded in moving Mum to a room with only one other lady and no television, and after a while she began to relax and look a little more comfortable. But the hospital, Ruth! I'm sure you remember the General. It was where Mike had his appendix removed when he was sixteen and where you got into such trouble with that stroppy nurse for smuggling him a ham sandwich before he had farted. To this day I still don't understand why it was so important that he passed wind before he ate. Luckily none of mine ever needed an appendectomy, as I'm sure I couldn't have resisted bringing them some nice titbits, wind or no wind.

But even the second ward was like a Victorian prison cell, with only one small window which was so far up the high wall that you could never see the sky, and painted that sickly green always used in hospitals although I can't think why - it even makes healthy people look as if they are at death's door. But that's the National Health for you. Tommy told me he'd heard about a medical survey carried out in America which showed that mental patients are significantly calmer if the walls of their hospitals and institutions are painted pale pink. Apparently pink is psychologically very soothing. Fancy that! I love pink, always have. Tommy said that that was probably why I was such a softy; it was all the pink I wore and surrounded myself with. Perhaps it was my subconscious protecting my 'inner calm.' Who knows? I'm sure he was just teasing; he loved to tease me as you know, but he never did it in a cruel way, unlike our father. Tommy was never unkind. In fact, he wouldn't know how to be. He is a rare creature, my Tommy, and it is he who is the softy. Perhaps that's what you didn't like, a gentle type of man, but it suits me very well.

It was years before Mum's accident when Dad decided to cancel their private medical health insurance. Thinking back, it was some time after the last property crash in 1991, if my memory serves me right, and Dad was full of 'the bloody Government take so much in tax that I'm blowed if they can't bloody well pay for me when I'm sick,' or some such thing. Anyway, they no longer had medical insurance and Tommy and I decided that we would be able to manage to get her the right care somehow or other. Dad, of course, remained obdurate and wasn't going to add a penny towards her medical bills; he had made up his mind, and that was that. But Tommy and I thought differently, and although Tommy pointed out to him just how much he had saved over the years by not buying medical insurance, Dad, being Dad, said that that had nothing to do with the argument; he had paid his taxes so the government should foot the bill. It didn't really matter; Tommy and I just paid the bills quietly rather than have another row, or run the risk of Mum suffering more unnecessary pain. We considered it all part of the process of life. Of course we had to use our savings, but as Tommy said "that's what savings are for Maisie, to use in emergencies, and Margaret needs our help now, doesn't she?" So we were happy to help out, and that was all there was to it. In any case it didn't cost much that time because as I said, I moved in with Mum and cared for her myself, but in her last year or two that wasn't possible.

So that's how Mum's slow decline began, and it's more than enough for one email.

With love,

Maisie

From: Ruth Braydon ruthbraydon@cedaw.com.ar
Date: 7th January 2011
To: Maisie Wilton maisiewilton@btinternet.com

Dear Maisie,

Thank you for your email. I do realise that it is an enormous task
I have asked you to do and I am extremely grateful that you are
taking the time to tell me. I did not know that Mum had broken
her hip as you rightly surmised. Did she recover fully? Was she
able to walk normally again?

In reply to your question about my work, yes, we do work in
teams which include a doctor, legal expert and other untrained but
caring types – just like you! Although we are largely groups of women, there is always one man with each group to handle the men.

On the subject of Tommy, I know he is just right for you. He
is a gentle type, full of empathy, as you say. Just not my type of
man, but then Billy wasn't a manly man as it turned out, either.
Please would you tell him how much I appreciate his generosity
of spirit when Mum broke her hip? What a stalwart, long suffering, uncomplaining couple you are! I can imagine the two of you
keeping quiet and just getting on with the caring and cleaning
and everything else you did for Mum during that time. It seems
to me that you have large amounts of inner strength, Maisie. No
more 'the little drip' if you ever were. Sentimental, certainly, but
to have had the sheer stamina to put up with the old man all
that time is something I could never have done, and I have always
been cast as the 'toughy.' How you can still excuse Dad is beyond me, unless he has softened with age. Did he reinstate private
medical insurance after Mum broke her hip, or did he just ex-

pect you and Tommy to continue to pay her medical bills? But of course, it was all ten years ago, so I will have to wait for you to tell me how he behaved as the years progressed.

I used to adore going to The Hoppings fair on the town moor. There was a wildly attractive gypsy who used to hang onto the tub seats on the ride that swung them around in circles while simultaneously going up and down, do you know the ride I mean? You hated it as it always made you feel sick, but my friend Gina and I adored it and would spend most of our pocket money on that ride. The gypsy would swirl the tubs seats of attractive young girls even faster, which he always did to ours, and we'd scream our heads off in fear and delight, laughing and flirting with him. I can still see him now. He had long jet black hair and bright blue eyes and wore a sleeveless black leather jerkin with nothing on underneath, which I thought was incredibly sexy. For weeks after the fair had gone, I fantasised about running away with him. I was under the strictest orders from Mum to take care of you, but I'm afraid I never did. Gina and I used to dump you on Mike and run off to the ride as fast was we could, every year dreading that our gorgeous gypsy would not be there any more.

Of course I remember Mungo's old cars! What you never knew, because you were far too young and innocent, was that he often used to give me a lift into town to the disco on his way home from the pub, *after* I had climbed out of my bedroom window. And he never spilled the beans. Good old Mungo!

I'm tired now and it is late, so I'll say goodbye and look forward to hearing from you again as soon as possible.

With love,

Ruth

From: Maisie Wilton maisiewilton@btinternet.com
Date: 15th January 2011
To: Ruth Braydonruthbraydon@cedaw.com.ar

Dear Ruth,

My apologies for taking so long to get back to you. There's been a great deal to do since Mum died, and it's taking much longer than I hoped. Dad doesn't know where any of the papers I need are kept, as Mum looked after the domestic side of things and he dealt with his business. It is a lesson to me that husbands and wives should share these matters. There is still so much to do. For example, I have to cancel her carers allowance and appointments with the specialists, and I can't face dealing with her clothes and personal belongings just yet, it still feels too raw, and Dad is not much use. No surprise there.

Goodness! You were even wilder than I thought! I'm amazed that you were never caught going out through your bedroom window. Dad would have gone ballistic! How on earth did you get back in? Did Mike come with you, or did you always go alone? You're much braver than I am, or ever could be. You always were. I'm glad my kids weren't as wild because I don't know how I would have handled it. They had so much baggage anyway that I think a safe and comfortable home was all they wanted after their terrible early years.

You asked if Dad behaved any better towards Mum as he aged. Yes, and no. Only in short spurts after a crisis, after which he would slip back into his usual behaviour, but he has recently become much less aggressive. He found it very difficult when I began to stand up to him. Yes! *Me!* But it was only in the last few years that I finally found the courage to do so. In any case he was never nasty to Mum, he worshipped her all his life as you know. As for medical care, no, he never reinstated their medical insurance and he never willingly put his hand in his pocket either. The couple of times it was mooted it was like a red rag to a bull. He ranted his usual spiel about paying too much tax and that the government should pay for all our health care, but by then I was beyond caring. My sole concern was to help our mother and make sure she was as comfortable and pain free as possible. Anyway, back to Mum.

After two more days in the cell-like ward, we were allowed to take Mum to recuperate at the Royal Victoria Infirmary, a vast improvement on the General. We felt so sorry for the lady in the other bed, who had become quite a friend by this time. She had no one to look after her, and had had no visitors; her only son lived in South Africa and so she was going to recuperate in a state nursing home. She was educated and softly spoken and like Mum, an avid reader. We kept in touch with her for years, visiting just once a week to make sure she was all right and taking her out on her birthday, and on sunny days for lunch at Marsden Rock, pushing her wheelchair along the promenade afterwards. She loved the sea and breathing in the fresh air and being able to "stretch her eyes to the horizon" as she used to say. Her son only came over to visit her once, about three months after she left hospital. She was never able to return to her flat and when he realised she would have to live in a home for the rest of her life, he flew back to sell it and pack up her belongings. She was very sad about this and Tommy and I did our best to collect her most precious things before her son threw them away, and took them to her room in the old people's home. She was so grateful it was pathetic, and we had only brought a few photographs and some letters and her nice dressing gown, plus a few other personal bits and pieces that meant so much to her. When she died four years later she left us £10,000 as a thank you. Tommy and I couldn't believe our eyes when we read the letter from her solicitor. We had only done what we did out of love for her, not for any other reason, although her son rather unkindly suggested that we had. She always had a warm smile, no matter how much pain she was in, just like our mother. She was a lesson to us all, Tommy always said whenever we talked about her, which we did often. Her name was Dorothea Lambert, and I loved it. To me it sounded like the name of a Victorian botanist or an author, perhaps a member of the Bloomsbury set. She wasn't anyone important during her life, just one of "the unsung heroes" as Tommy described her. A self contained, uncomplaining person with a tremendous sense of humour and a British stiff upper lip, she'd worked for years with lepers in India and when she returned home she spent the rest of her life doing good works. Quietly, with no fanfare. Just beavering away trying to ease the burden of others. And of course we saved the money and had it to spend when Mum needed a carer, which we thought was just what Dorothea would have approved.

The x-ray hadn't shown conclusively that Mum had broken her hip and the consultant was very dismissive. He told us that in all likelihood she had, and that she should just go home and rest, as it would heal itself in six weeks. Bones take six weeks to heal, as I'm sure you know. So we took her home in our car and Tommy lugged a single bed from the guest room into the dining room so that she didn't have to climb those treacherously steep stairs every evening. But Dad made quite a fuss about it, saying that he wasn't going to eat in the kitchen like a workman because he couldn't get into the dining room. Of course Mum felt very bad about this, as she would, so we crammed her bed into the corner beside the window in order that Dad could sit down at the end of the table to eat in comfort.

On Christmas day, only about three months after her accident, Mum had a TIA in our sitting room. A TIA, in case you don't know, stands for a Transient Ischemic Attack, which is like a mini stroke usually caused by a tiny blood clot. She had come over for Christmas lunch - we made Christmas lunch at our house from that year onwards - and she was sitting talking to Joy, who was only about fourteen at the time, when she suddenly began to talk gobbledegook. Joy shouted out for me, but by the time I came in from the kitchen - I had been basting the turkey and had to put it back in the oven - she was all right again. It was Tommy who realised what had happened, but she recovered very quickly and to our amazement, told us that although she couldn't get her words out, she understood everything we said to her. We were all rather shaken up, especially Joy, but we gave everyone a glass of champagne and not much more than an hour later, we were all sitting around the table tucking into an enormous meal as if nothing had happened. Mum went home straight after the Queen's speech to rest, and the doctor came the day after Boxing Day and confirmed that more than likely she had had a TIA. She had one or two more after that, years later, but by that time she was much less physically able.

By New Year the pain in her hip had become acute and her doctor recommended a second x-ray. Tommy and I took her back to the R.V.I. and this time the X-ray showed quite clearly that her hip *had* been broken and had not mended properly and that was the cause of her increasing pain, which I know I would have been unable to bear, but Mum was always a silent sufferer. She hadn't rested enough while it was healing, and as soon as she could move she began looking after Dad, cooking and doing the washing and ironing once more, despite our protestations. Of course it turned out to be a disaster and the result was she had to have three long screws inserted into her hip to secure it, which meant another hospital stay. But this time, much to her relief, we managed to get her into the Freeman Hospital as soon as she had her operation, and she was reasonably comfortable there. The care at the Freeman is much better than the R.V.I. and she was so impressed by it, as we all were, that I persuaded Jane to try to get a job there, which she did. Jane still works there and is very happy.

Mike came over from Sydney while she was still in the Freeman, and stayed with us. He visited her every afternoon for a week which gave her enormous pleasure, and Dad went in the evenings so they never once ran into each other.

It was heaven see Mike after so many years. He is a little stouter than he used to be, but is still tall and very good looking and his dark hair has become a beautiful silver. He has what he calls an "Australian permatan" and has developed quite an Australian accent, but after so many years, it's hardly surprising. He brought photographs of his children; Bruce, the eldest, was 25 then and working as a doctor in Sydney hospital, but his real interest is in psychiatry and he is taking further exams to become a clinical psychiatrist. He is an extremely handsome young man as so many mixed race people are, with bright blue eyes and mahogany wavy hair and a deep gold complexion. He's always surrounded by adoring girls, so Mike told us, but has a lovely girl-friend whom he hopes to marry one day. She is a paediatrician at

Sydney hospital, so we are becoming quite a medical family. His daughter Amber was 23, and exquisite. She is very artistic and runs a gallery in Sydney which sells modern Australian art which apparently is very fashionable and fetches enormous prices. She is frequently stopped in the street by model scouts and asked if she wants to work for them, but she is too well educated and not interested in such "fluff" as Mike says she calls it. She's a serious person and is becoming more and more involved in politics, much to both Mike's admiration and dismay. It is very hard for a woman to make an impact in Australian politics, he says, and her good looks will go against her, as no one will take a beautiful woman seriously. She is predominantly interested in the disadvantaged and ethnic minorities, above all the Aborigines, and is doing her best to represent them in her free time. So she is thinking of leaving her well paid job and standing for Parliament and Mike and Sheena are supporting her all the way. Of course Sheena knows all about being an unwanted immigrant and an ethnic minority. You only have to glance at her background as a Ugandan Asian having to flee Idi Amin and his heinous regime, to know what she has suffered. Australia has been wonderful to her and the whole Jhaveri family she says, helping them settle and create a new life, so she is delighted that her daughter wants to put something back into her adopted country. Although Mike is very proud of Amber, he thinks she could do so much more for those in need by keeping her high profile job and quietly lobbying the rich and influential people who she meets in the art gallery. But Amber sees things differently and will no doubt make a success of whatever she turns her hand to. It is such a tragedy that Dad has only very recently met them, but that's his loss and there is nothing we can do about it. Back to the leopard and his spots.

Mike began to come home every year after Mum broke her hip. He hadn't been over for eight years before that and vowed he would never leave it so long again. He remained true to his word and has brought his whole family over several times since then. The first time was a year after Mum broke her hip ten years ago, and the last time was just before she died. Mum was so happy to meet his wife and children, and welcomed them all with open arms, just as you would expect. They stayed in a small, comfortable local hotel, as our house is much too small and we were already bursting at the seams with our own children, before your Ricky moved in with his troubles taking up most of our time and money. But when Mike came on his own he always stayed with us and it was a very precious time for me having him all to myself in my own home, with no one to disturb us. I learned all about Mike's life in Australia and he also gave me sound professional advice regarding Ricky, who was going through a very bad time. We would talk for hours each time he came, reminiscing our childhood and youth and what it had meant to us, understanding each other's point of view as adults with the benefit of hindsight, and why he still wouldn't see Dad again, no matter what. Although I understood his feelings and respected them, I couldn't help but feel sad. That's the 'wet me' again I suppose, isn't it? But I do think that we ought to learn from life and forgive and forget, not carry bad memories and grudges along with us like a cancer gnawing at our spirits, eating up all the goodness inside us. But Mike doesn't think so. He prefers to put things behind him but refuses to be reconciled to the past. His philosophy is one of "looking forward" he says, and perhaps that's the best way for him, but I need to forgive and let go before I can move on. What about you, Ruth?

Can you believe that a couple of times during the first few visits, Tommy would find us still at the kitchen table when he came home from work in the evening? We had been there all day! There was so much to say, so much ground to cover and we had to fill every moment, as our precious time together was extremely limited. Tommy didn't mind, he just laughed his head off when he found us sitting in exactly the same place as he had left us, nine hours before, surrounded by a sea of empty teacups. He poured us a glass of wine and offered to make dinner or buy us all a takeaway. It was always the same. Mike hankered after "good old British fish and chips" as he called it. He missed it in Australia and so we tucked into huge plates of deep fried cod and chips from 'The Salty Sailor,' the fish and chippy in Jesmond, eating them straight from the newspaper, covered in salt and vinegar and laughing all the time at how much Dad would have disapproved! The kids loved it too as we allowed them to eat with their fingers, and I loved it because there was no washing up to do afterwards. But the smell the next day was terrible and we all suffered from indigestion. Luckily I had plenty of Alka-Seltzer to dispense in the morning. It was such a special time.

Of course Dad knew Mike was over and staying with us, but he never mentioned it. Mum had new photos of Mike and his family in her hospital room and then later in her bedroom and although Dad never commented on them, he didn't remove them either. That would have broken her heart and have been a step too far even for her, longsuffering though she was, and he didn't dare. So we carried on without ever mentioning Mike, and I know you will not approve of the way we behaved, but it was by far the easiest all-round, believe me. Honesty is a fine thing, but sometimes it is better to keep silent on matters that are too painful to discuss. There is far too much of this so called 'sharing' these days. People often want to 'share' even when the recipient makes it quite clear he doesn't want to be shared with. Is this yet another weak excuse, I hear you ask? Maybe. But we try to do what we can with the least damage to all concerned, Ruth. At least that is the view to which Tommy and I adhere, for better or for worse.

I'll send this off now and write again in a few days. In the meantime I send you my love as always,

Maisie

From: Ruth Braydon ruthbraydon@cedaw.com.ar
Date: 16th January 2011
To: Maisie Wilton maisiewilton@btinternet.com

Dear Maisie,

You slipped into your last email that "Ricky had moved in and was taking up all your time and money with his troubles." And that he was having a very bad time and Mike gave you sound advice, without saying a word about what was going on. *What do you mean?* He certainly shouldn't have had any money problems; Billy was a very successful musician, so why did he need your money? What happened to him? Has he been very ill? And why did he move in with you? Where was Billy while all this was going on? Please tell me, Maisie. I am helplessly waiting for your explanation.

But I was glad to hear that Jane is all right and at the Freeman. So she passed all her nursing exams. Good for her. She was such a solid, reliable child, always was. Sometimes I used to wonder which was the mother and which the child. Even when she was only tiny! She certainly doesn't have many of my genes. Just as well, in more ways than one.

And I was also glad to have news of Mike and his family. What a shock for Dad to discover that he had married an African Asian! Ha! I can just imagine his incandescent fury when he found out. Serves the old bugger right! I wish I'd been there when he found out. But you said they only met very recently? It must have been rather like a Feydeau farce, Mike arriving at the front door as Dad sneaked furtively out of the back of the house! Such utter nonsense, but sadly, so like our family.

Of course I cannot agree with you about not always being honest, as you will no doubt remember. Nor can I "forgive and forget." I'm with Mike on that point. I remain unrelenting in my not forgiving of our father, which is why I value the work I do here, helping abused women free themselves from the tyranny of their bullying men. But there's the rub. Do I expect my own family to forgive me for my sudden departure and silence? Ah well, it's all far too late now. Tell me, did Billy find someone else? I do hope so, not just because it would ease my guilt but genuinely, I mean it for his happiness. I only wish that he has found his perfect partner, as I found mine.

I'm glad that you and Tommy kept the £10,000 from Dorothea as you have implied that you really needed it later. It sounds as if Dorothea's son could have been Dad's relation in his reaction to his own mother. But I was horrified to learn that Dad still refused to pay for her care. Appalling and mean though he is, I am nonetheless shocked that he even baulked at paying for his wife, whom we all agree he adored, *despite* his stupid argument about the government paying for their health care. But actually, come to think of it, he *was* incredibly mean to her *indirectly,* through *us,* which had exactly the same effect. He must have hurt her all her life with his meanness and bullying of his children. For heaven's sake, he even drove their only son to the other side of the world! And what is even more curious is that Dad was always kind and generous to his own parents and brothers and sister. I could never understand why he couldn't have been as open hearted and open handed to us.

You were such a serious little thing when we were young. Mike and I used to talk about you often, spending hours huddled together trying to work out how we could protect you from our bullying father. But by the time Mike was a teenager it took all his strength just to stand up for himself, so it was left to me to do most of the fighting for you both. At least, that's what I tried to do, to stand in the direct line of fire to protect you from the fallout, until I left home, which I did as soon as I possibly could. I wonder if you were even aware of my efforts.

Write very soon and tell me about Ricky, please, Maisie.

Your loving sister,

Ruth

From: Maisie Wilton maisiewilton@btinternet.com
Date: 17th January 2011
To: Ruth Braydon ruthbraydon@cedaw.com.ar

Dear Ruth,

So some of all that fighting and arguing with Dad was for my benefit! And I always thought you were *against* me, Ruth, because I
knew you couldn't stand my being so "wet" or a pathetic "drip" as
you called it, nor my frequent crying and emotion. I also always
assumed that the rows you and Dad had behind the slammed sitting room door were about you, *your* demands and injustices, and
had nothing to do with me! You were always so fiery and brave; it
seemed to me that nothing would stop you from achieving your
own aims, no matter what obstacles lay in your path. And I still
believe I am right on that point. The very fact that you are living
in Buenos Aires proves it. As you so beautifully described us, you
are a lion hearted "Scarlet O'Hara" character and I, a meek and
mild "Melanie". I have grown stronger and much more determined over the years, but still always opt for peace and a quiet life.

You're right about Dad. I have never thought of it from that
point of view. Of course he must have made her unhappy by his
meanness to us, but as she never complained and always tried to
excuse him, I didn't consider it must have hurt her very much. I
suppose his bullying of her was subliminal.

You have asked me to tell you about Ricky, but it will be very
difficult Ruth, because I feel that if I am going to embark on the
task, I should tell you the whole truth as it happened, or at least
as I experienced it. But I must express *most profoundly* that I am
only the messenger. Life can be very difficult and complicated

and we each must follow our own path, wherever it takes us. Even if it is to another continent. So before I begin, I ask you to understand that I was only doing my best, and that I was incredibly naive and ignorant in many areas in those days. Tommy and I have had to learn the hard way. It seems life offers no other option. But before I begin, I want to take away any anxiety regarding his health. You asked if he had been ill. Well, in a way he has. But not with cancer or anything like that, so don't worry on that score.

When you left to work in Argentina, Ricky was still only sixteen. I know that you had left him and Jane in the care of their father and, if it ever became necessary, had even appointed Tommy and me to be their legal guardians, which we were happy to be. Billy continued to make plenty of money as a bass guitarist and so money was never an issue. But there is more to life than money and when you neither returned nor even contacted them, they naturally felt abandoned, too. The shock of your brutal, dismissive letter to Billy, without any letter of explanation or kind words to them, reiterating your love for *them,* at least, proved to be a much greater hurdle for them to adjust to than your decision never to return. At sixteen and not quite nineteen there is little tolerance or understanding of the deficiencies and transgressions of others, particularly for one's own parents, and frequently there is no forgiveness, even in later life. After all, both you and Mike remain unforgiving of our father. The Chinese 'long view' comes with maturity and experience, and some, like our own father, for example, never get there. I know you explained to them why you were going and what you were going to do, but it was done with indecent haste Ruth, if I may say so, and no sooner had you told them than you bolted out of the door, leaving me to tell our parents and pick up the pieces. You thought they were old enough to cope with your leaving *for only a year*, and I can see your point of view. They probably would have coped if it had only been a year and if you had kept in contact, but you did neither. They were devastated by your betrayal of your family and also extremely angry with you, particularly when it eventually began to come out in the press, although Billy pleaded with the press to leave your children alone. It seems he was better known than we thought. Even if some people deserve to be vilified, I do not think that crucifixion by the tabloids should be condoned. It is too much akin to a public hanging. We all know that sort of invasive cruelty creates the type of prurient titillation that sells newspapers, so I doubt it will ever stop because human beings love an opportunity to indulge in *schadenfreude*. We are a preternaturally savage species and the only one of which I am aware that enjoys the misery of its own kind for no other purpose that its own gratification - unless David Attenborough has recently discovered a hitherto unknown cruelty gene within the animal kingdom.

Your own childhood had been much tougher on a day-to-day basis, although you never had to deal with anything like the desertion of your mother. At least our parents were always *there*, although not always for the better. But your leaving obviously did not only adversely affect your children. Billy was shattered by your letter and he rapidly fell to pieces. He adored you Ruth - you were his rock - and he could not understand why you had so suddenly, and brutally, deserted them. As you hadn't replied to any letters he was at a complete loss to know what to do. The only point of contact we had *at all* was the single address you left behind and as you never replied we could only presume you were no longer there. And Argentina is far too big a country for anyone to have scoured in search of you, although we discussed it many, many times; and so we could do nothing but wait in impotence to hear from you.

Billy became deeply depressed and increasingly unable to support his children emotionally. What made matters worse was that he assumed that their shared grief would bring them together, but it did not because he became such a pathetic figure. Every evening he collapsed on the sofa in a heap of despair, wailing about being rejected, and it shocked and disgusted them. They couldn't bear it, or the way he clung to them. After all, they had to deal with their own pain and they certainly couldn't bear the added burden of watching their own father unravelling before them. So Billy felt rejected by them too and adversely reacted by taking up session work again and going on lengthy tours, resulting in Jane and Ricky being effectively abandoned by both their parents.

This put Jane in a very difficult position. She was still only nineteen at the time and I know that you thought that at nineteen you had already been independent for two years, and she should therefore be able to cope; but Jane suddenly had the responsibility of her younger brother in his A level year and the house to run, as well as training to be a nurse. Of course you were right about Jane, she *was* up to it, even though she was often pushed to the point of despair, and she has turned out to be a remarkable young woman. But not without great cost to her and Ricky.

Consequently Ricky was often left on his own at home. Jane had to work hard and when she was at home she also had to cook their evening meal and see to the household bills and the washing and ironing and worst of all, deal with the almost daily complaints about Ricky from his school. After you left he began to slide downhill but he did manage to pass his 'AS' exams, not through hard work, but because he is bright and an extremely fast learner. But not far into the autumn term of his last school year he began truanting and hanging out with a rough crowd he had met during the summer holidays, none of whom did any school work and who encouraged him to ignore it, too. It was as if he simply gave up any idea of education or ambition, or even making the effort to keep clean. He began to lose weight and started to look gaunt and grey. I don't think he ate if Jane didn't cook a meal for him and although she left him food to heat in the microwave if she were on night duty, she told me he rarely bothered to eat it.

Jane did her utmost to keep them going, and did a very good job for over a year before she came to Tommy and me to ask for help. It was on Halloween night, and she was beside herself. We almost didn't open the door, as there had been so many kids ringing the doorbell demanding a 'trick or treat', and we had decided that we'd had quite enough for one night. But Jane pressed the doorbell as if she were tolling Doomsday until we finally relented and answered it. There she stood, tearstained and shaking with cold and fear, and of course we took her in immediately and put the kettle on, wrapping her up in a warm blanket, but before the kettle had even boiled, the whole story began to pour out.

She was at her wits' end. Ricky had only just scraped through the first half of term and had hardly been to school at all since the summer, and the headmaster was about to throw him out for good. She was in the middle of her second year nursing exams and didn't know which way to turn. What was worse was she suspected him of taking some kind of drugs. She wasn't sure what, but apparently he often acted in an erratic manner when he was at home and when he was like that she couldn't get any sense out of him. She looked ghastly, exhausted and white faced, with huge dark circles beneath her eyes. Tommy and I were appalled. We had seen them frequently since you left because they were invited to join us every Sunday for a good meal, a roast of something or other with our kids, and they had seemed more or less fine, under the circumstances. But that night Jane looked like a frightened young girl from a Dickens novel, a half starved Little Dorritt, and we were shocked at the change in her. I learned later that they had made a super human effort to be normal and nicely dressed on those Sundays. Jane had insisted on it, and forced Ricky to come and behave himself. Years later he told us that it was the only few hours of peace and comfort he had during the entire week.

Once she had let down her guard it was like seeing a completely different person. No holes barred. The real Jane exposed. Apparently this had been going on for months and she had tried her best to cope alone, knowing that Tommy and I were looking after Mum and had our own, often difficult kids to care for. By that time we were fostering four children, and all of them had problems at one time or another, and I think this had been the reason we had been blind to the difficulties Jane was dealing with. I hope that was the case, but you know how it is. One becomes so involved in one's own life that sometimes it is almost impossible to see outside one's own immediate anxieties. Although even writing about it years later still makes me think that's a pathetic excuse. So we took her in and made her a cup of hot, sweet tea, and listened to what she had to say, poor lamb. And that was where it all began.

I'm shattered now, Ruth, and must go to bed. It is after midnight and reliving the past is not always a pleasant experience. But I have promised to tell you everything and I will....but it will take time.

Until the next letter.

With my love,

Maisie

P.S. Billy did find someone else. A very nice woman called Susan, and he seems happy again, at last.

From: Ruth Braydon ruthbraydon@cedaw.com.ar
Date: 25th January 2011
To: Maisie Wilton maisiewilton@btinternet.com

Dear Maisie,

I'm sorry I have taken so long to reply, but I have not been well. However, I have rallied a little again and am well enough to write.

But to your email, which ended very dramatically with 'and that was where it all began.' Where all *what* began? What I have read only so far is bad enough. Thank you for telling me, as I do realise that I don't deserve the huge effort you will have to put into telling me, and I appreciate it enormously, particularly as no one else is going to tell me. But having said that, you have been quite judgemental Maisie, despite your protestations to the contrary. Perhaps you did not realise it, but it came across that way. No doubt I deserve it.

Poor Jane. What a lot she had to deal with, and so young, too. I did leave home at seventeen, but of course I admit that I didn't have to deal with the difficulties that faced Jane; mine were purely financial, just trying to keep body and soul together while I was at university.

And Ricky, my beautiful son, why did he take it so hard so early on? I know that boys are supposed to be hooked on their mothers, but I'll confess at last that I was never a natural mother. In retrospect I should probably never have married, but I did my best in this, for me, foreign land. And when I left Ricky was a healthy, outgoing bright boy who loved his football and music, and was popular and clever at school with great expectations for a place at a top university, so I thought I had done my duty. There has to be *some time* in a woman's life where she has the freedom to do what *she* wants, surely? A brief respite between bringing up children before you begin caring for elderly parents and helping with grandchildren, and if you don't grab it, it will be too late - you will have arrived at old age yourself and the opportunity will be lost forever.

I was so sad to read what you had to say about Billy and the kids. I would never have imagined that Billy would have fallen apart like that. He always loved his home life and our children, and I rather thought it was his turn to hold the fort. Anyway, I'm glad he has found his Susan.

Billy, Jane and Ricky were always so close and if anyone was the odd one out in our family, it was *me*. Those three were far more akin to each other than they were to me. Sometimes I felt as if I were living in a land of strangers. Actually, I felt like that most of the time. And I had imagined and planned in my mind that they would continue to get on with their own lives, just as they had always done. They were not children, after all! And Billy had his career to occupy him. Despite being a bass guitarist and spending most of his time with wild rock and roll performers, he was the sort of person who really only wanted to be at home. When he was on tour he would phone me *every day* telling me how much he wished he were at home with his family, eating baked beans on toast in front of the TV or playing football with the kids, instead of being dragged off to some exotic, exclusive night club till the early hours in the morning with the other musicians. It astounded me – and really irritated me too, adding salt into my already opened wound, because I longed to dance wildly till dawn with coke-snorting pop stars and film stars, without any responsibility! It was what I imagined our life would continue to be when I married him, so I was bitterly disappointed early on in my marriage when I discovered his true nature; and once I had children, my fate was sealed. That type of caring behaviour is much more your department. I do not now, nor did I ever want to be needed. It only makes me want to run a mile in the opposite direction! I expect you will find that shocking, Maisie. And my guess is that most women married to a rock guitarist would be only too pleased to know that their husband was faithful and adoring, but not me. I was born independent and I can't help it, it's just my nature. Perhaps this side of my personality comes directly from Dad. I would be an appalling carer, and on that single point alone, I can sympathise with him. So when my chance came to do something really interesting and different, I didn't think twice.

But I am very surprised at what you have told me. *Very surprised.* And disappointed too. You may think it is because I was even more detached from the whole 'family and bringing up the children thing,' than even *I* realised. And as for the drugs, well, it's a right of passage, isn't it? Did you, may I suggest gently, take it all a bit too seriously, Maisie? I am *not* criticising, just inquiring. Anyway, tell me how it all turned out in your next letter. All this happened years ago, after all, although you finish your letter with "and this is where it all began."

In great anticipation,

With love,

Ruth

From: Maisie Wilton maisiewilton@btinternet.com
Date: 29th January 2011
To: Ruth Braydon ruthbraydon@cedaw.com.ar

Forgive me, Ruth. I find I just can't continue Ricky's story. Not yet at any rate. It is too long and complicated and although I know that I must tell you everything, I fear it will take much longer than I first thought, and, it appears, will be much more taxing for me to write down than I had envisaged. I promise to tell you everything, but not just yet. And to be frank, you really took the wind out of me with your comment about my taking Ricky's drug taking too seriously. I found it deeply upsetting, if not downright offensive. In fact it made me very angry. After all, it was *you* who left *me* to hold the fort on *every front* and it is utterly inappropriate for you to judge me when you know nothing yet. You should wait until I have told you everything first. You were always too quick to judge, just like our father, and you, above all, are in no position to judge, Ruth, if *I* might now be allowed to pass judgement. And you always had to be right. Neither you, nor Dad, could stand to be contradicted. Both of you saw everything in black and white, whereas in reality, life is one grey mass of conciliation. Consider war. War between countries and war within families. The same applies. Peace is most often attained through mediation and diplomacy, rarely on the battlefield. And anyway, winning the war does not guarantee achieving peace between nations, nor families. It takes tremendous effort and patience on both sides. So please don't pass judgement on me until I have had time to tell you everything that happened, and also keep in mind that it was *you* who went shooting off into the great blue yonder, like some giddy schoolgirl leaving all her responsibilities behind, while I remained at home to look after *your* family and our parents on top of my own. For most women there is never a time when they are free from care. And most of us just have to get on with it. Hindsight is a wonderful thing, Ruth. If I sound thoroughly rattled and hurt, it is because that is exactly how I feel. But I'll get over it. I am almost over it now, which is why I have picked up my pen once more, so to speak.

I confess I was utterly taken aback by your email on so many fronts. First, I had absolutely *no idea* that your marriage was such a huge disappointment. We thought you had everything! A beautiful house, plenty of money, lovely holidays abroad, things Tommy and I could never afford and at times, I admit, sometimes I felt terribly jealous of you, particularly when you had your own two lovely children. And secondly, I was completely oblivious until now that you found motherhood so trying. It left me thoroughly shaken, and made me wonder if I know who you are at all. Why didn't you say something, Ruth? I would have done my very best to help in whatever way I could. We were all rather relieved when Billy *did not* turn out to be a typical rock guitarist, despite Dad's conviction it would all end in tears. We knew you loved travel and adventure, but now I see we falsely assumed that as you were twenty-six when you married, you had grown out of it and were ready to settle down. And you had an interesting job at university. But none of us knew that you found domestic stability so stultifying and soul destroying. Did you really find motherhood and working as a university lecturer so unrewarding? Never once did you even hint at these enormous problems and I found that despite myself I had to admire you for soldiering on for so long. Most women these days would have left long before you did and so I began to wonder why you had stayed, if you had been so unhappy and frustrated.

I find it quite incredible that you cannot grasp the pain and damage your silence created. And that you blindly refuse to acknowledge the result of your actions. It wasn't your departure, Ruth, it was your *silence*. Nothing speaks louder than silence, and we were deafened by yours for *ten years*. Why didn't you write? I do not understand, Ruth. And what made you stay and not come back as you had originally intended after a maximum of a year? You're working in a field where women have been let down, abused and tormented by their husbands and families and yet, incomprehensibly, you seem unable to acknowledge that your own behaviour might have a similar affect on your own children. I fail to see how you cannot make the connection. There are many kinds of abuse as you know; after all you have made it your specialty.

Love

Maisie

From: Ruth Braydon ruthbraydon@cedaw.com.ar
Date: 1st February 2011
To: Maisie Wilton maisiewilton@btinternet.com

Dear Maisie,

Ouch! You certainly made your feelings clear, and quite right too! *Forgive me,* please. I'm afraid blunt speaking has always been a great fault of mine which I cannot seem to cure. Sometimes I call a spade a 'bloody shovel' but I never intended any harm - it was meant as gentle teasing, about the drugs, I mean. Billy and I smoked dope for years before we had children, and quite often afterwards, but we never got involved in hard drugs like so many musicians. It just wasn't for us, thank God, as we have lost so many friends over the years.

I see you *have* changed! When did you become so bold? So. O.K. I'll take a deep breath and keep my feelings to myself until I hear everything. But please remember that it's very difficult to receive such news so long after the events have taken place and not comment. How could it be otherwise? How would you have responded if the shoe had been on the other foot? That sounds like justification, but I can't just read your letters and not make any comment or judgement *at all.* Surely you would not expect that of me? I will endeavour to soften my responses, but I will, of course, respond. Indeed, it would be unnatural not to. So I shall ask you to forgive me in advance.

I'll try and explain myself so we can get it out of the way, as I badly want you to tell me about Jane and Ricky.

To start with, how could I *possibly* have complained about the daily drudgery of motherhood and my disappointment with my marriage to you, *of all people*? You and Tommy were devoted to each other and had dedicated your lives to children, and *disabled* children at that, and then you fostered mixed-race children from problem backgrounds. And there was I, living in clover, with two beautiful children of my own and plenty of money, while you two struggled so valiantly to keep your fragile ship afloat. I never knew how you did it, Maisie. I watched in astonishment and growing admiration as you spread your kindness to so many needy people, so how could I possibly have come whining to you? And I'm glad I never did, now that I know you struggled with feelings of jealousy from time to time.

I've confessed I found being a mother of young children very trying. It was so endlessly *boring*. Particularly after all the fun Billy and I had had before we were married. Do you remember all those trips we took to L.A. and Australia and so many other places when I accompanied Billy on tour, or visited him wherever he was recording? It seemed I had found my perfect world, and we had so much *fun!* He earned very good money, travelled a great deal with very creative, exciting and interesting people, musicians mostly, and yet had none of the pain of fame. I think it was Billy's *ordinariness* that kept him in constant demand, apart from his superb musicianship, of course. He never lost control and he was utterly reliable, always turning up for sessions on time, never missing a gig, unlike so many pop musicians. He was, and still is, I presume, a highly respected musician, but because he was never attached to a band, he managed to keep a fairly low profile, except in the music business. I used to think he was the musician's equivalent of a script writer. A wonderful film is only as good as its script, and yet how many script writers can you name? See what I mean? Even after we were married I travelled with him the moment the university broke for the holidays, and we continued our wonderful life staying in five star hotels in stunning locations until I became pregnant. And then it all came to an abrupt end. Boom. Just like that. And I fell hard and fast from a great height only to discover that blissful domesticity was what Billy had really wanted all along. His own family were a sorry, dysfunctional lot and he had always craved a stable home with a loving wife and children, whereas I had longed to escape our very controlling father and orderly home life with meals on the table at exactly the same time every single day.

But of course it wasn't *all* bad. Once the children went to school and I could go back to work at university, life became much easier. But those long, endless holidays which seemed to whip around every other week were often quite a trial. What had once been the time when I would joyfully leave to join Billy, he now went without me, and I was left alone with the children trying to think of something fun to do, day after day. I know we often had lovely holidays with our well off musician friends staying at their villas and on their boats, but it would be only two or three weeks out of a ten week holiday. I yearned for the bright, intellectually stimulating conversations with other dons and their frequent mild flirtations, and challenging debates with my students, but most of all I missed all the crazy fun we had had with our musician friends in exotic places. And there was Billy moaning down the phone, wanting only to come home and be cosseted, when all I wanted to do was grab my passport and run! And you thought I had had twenty years of contentment. Well, I was never the type to whinge. Some small saving grace.

As for my work, after fifteen years as a lecturer it had become rather dull and predictable, and CEDAW offered a wonderful opportunity to work at the coalface, starting a project from scratch.

And now, about my silence. Suffice it to say, my circumstances changed in a way I had not envisaged. Life is so unpredictable. I can only repeat that when I left I fully intended to stay for a year at the very most, but as the days turned into months I found I could not bear to read any more of your letters, let alone answer them, so I buried myself in silence until it was far, far too late, except to write to Billy and release him. I thought that by doing so I had done him a favour, believe it or not. In some ways it wasn't that difficult to remain silent. I was so far away in a completely different culture with nothing to remind me of home. I was entirely immersed in my work, and I discovered I had the capacity to completely shut myself off from everything to do with my old life, even my family. I expect that you will find that incomprehensible, but it was what happened. I wonder if for explorers, for example, it necessitates the same attitude of mind when they sail away on voyages of discovery for years at a time, leaving their loved ones behind with no guarantee that they would ever return. Perhaps it's not as uncommon as one might think. Maybe it's only unusual in a woman. Denial is an extremely powerful emotion, and a great help when one wants to escape mental anguish.

I have tried to explain why I did what I did, Maisie. I have done my best to be truthful and expansive, even though I still don't think my departure should have created such a fallout in my family. I mean kids grow up and leave home, don't they? They grow out of needing their parents, everyone does, so why should I shoulder all the blame? I do acknowledge that it was my silence that made you all so unhappy and angry and I hope I have explained my reason for it. But as you yourself have said, life is full of complications and is seldom as it appears on the surface. I hope it helps you to understand me a little better and does not make you hate me even more as a result. Now please can we return to what happened to Ricky after I left?

With much love and gratitude for what I am asking you to do,

Ruth

From: Maisie Wilton maisiewilton@btinternet.com
Date: 4th February 2011
To: Ruth Braydon ruthbraydon@cedaw.com.ar

Dear Ruth,

Thank you for your explanations - some things are much clearer now. But you clearly still don't get it, do you? Yes, kids grow up and leave home, but *parents* don't! I feel that someone has to tell you what your leaving did to your family, and it seems because I am the only one in communication with you, it has to be me, again. You had everything, Ruth. The lovely house, beautiful clothes, exotic holidays, and most important of all, your own beautiful children and a very loving husband. And you just threw it all away and walked out. But you left three very hurt and bitter people behind you, and you gaily assumed I would take care of everything. Just like that, so you could go and fulfil your fantasies. And you still haven't explained *why* you stayed, only why you *went*.

So I will tell you about Ricky and hope that will make you understand what misery and damage your disappearance caused. But I must warn you Ruth, it is *not* nice.

I had got as far as telling you about the dreadful Halloween night when Jane came to us in despair. Billy had hardly been at home for the best part of six months, and had taken to touring all the time, and when he wasn't touring he was away recording, often in America. He could hardly cope himself and gave no support to his children, apart from money.

Well anyway, after that night, Tommy and I decided we must take Ricky to live with us as Jane couldn't, and shouldn't, have to struggle alone any more. It was 1st November 2000 and you had been gone about fourteen months. We drove over to your house and helped him pack up his things and we made a room for him in Tommy's study, and Tommy moved his laptop, papers and so on into a small corner of the sitting room. We still had all the kids at home then. Alec has his own tiny single room and was twenty, and was in his last year at University reading economics. Sharon was fourteen, Sadie was twelve, and little Joy had just turned eleven. It was a tight squeeze as our house isn't very large, as you know, but we managed just fine once we got used to it. We used to say it was just like living on board a ship, where everyone is huggermugger all the time. It was at best cosy and intimate, and at worst, bedlam! There were seven people around the dinner table every evening, of which five were hungry, growing children, and it seemed to me that I lived in the supermarket and with my head bent over the washing machine during those years. I'm not complaining, Ruth. It was what Tommy and I had chosen, but it was a very tiring time.

Ricky looked awful once his mask was down, very thin, with huge black circles under his eyes. We made an appointment to visit his headmaster having decided to tell him the whole truth. It seemed the right and fair thing to do if we were to get him to help Ricky. Mr Adams was very kind, but it took us over an hour to persuade him to give Ricky one last chance.

'He's a very bright boy,' he told us, 'but he's hardly been to school for the past year and is way behind in all his subjects. Unless he works extremely hard, I don't think he has the slightest chance of even passing his A levels, let alone getting good enough grades for university. Could you provide him with some coaching? If he works all weekend, he just might have a chance, but I doubt it. I hate to see such a good brain going to waste. He had a very good future ahead of him and it would be a tragedy for him if he can't buckle down and get back on track. He's a natural at sciences, and I think that his passion and interest in the subject has kept his head above water, but only just. The trouble is, his teachers have all but given up on him, but I will try to

bring them round - although it won't be easy. Perhaps if you allow me to explain his circumstances I might elicit some sympathy for the boy.'

Of course we agreed, and feeling full of hope, we went home and told Ricky the good news that evening. But Ricky was not impressed. In fact he was very angry with us for telling Mr Adams about his family, which he considered deeply private, and no one had the right to tell anyone else except himself.

'I'm sorry, Ricky,' said Tommy. 'We did what we thought was the best for you, lad, that's all. At least he'll take you back, and I hope that you'll change your ways and work hard and do well. It was done for your own good, you know.'

Ricky glowered at Tommy and I tried to smooth things over. 'You've a home here now Ricky, and we love you with all our hearts. We'll support you in every way we can. We know it's not going to be easy. But you can get better now and I'll feed you up and take care of you, darling.'

How naïve we were! We didn't know that Ricky had been drinking hard for over a year and had become dependent on alcohol and dope, but we found out pretty quickly. He went out every night after dinner and we were unable to stop him. I realise how feeble that sounds, but how do you stop a large seventeen-year-old from going out if he wants to? He was young, and although he was thin, he was strong, and the determination to get a drink and have a smoke made him even stronger. That's why I was so annoyed when the government decided to fine, and even imprison parents of truanting children. It's all very well to force them to go to school when they are small, but once they reach their teens and are at the age they are most likely to truant, how on earth is a single mother supposed to drag her large, reluctant son or daughter out of bed in the morning?

He told us that he *had* to see his friends and we couldn't keep him locked up like a prisoner, particularly since he was nearly eighteen. So Tommy and I justified our decision to allow him to go out after dinner by agreeing that he did need some time out from his studies, and we reluctantly acquiesced. For a time he managed to get up in the morning and stay at school, but each morning it became harder and harder to rouse him. I had given him his own house key and most nights I lay awake in bed, waiting to hear it turn in the lock. He came home later and later and I could hear him crashing around in his room before silence fell, and only then did I feel able to go to sleep. Consequently Tommy and I became increasingly tired and Tommy began to look grey and permanently worn out, and I worried about the strain on him. But Tommy dismissed my fears and said that he would catch up at the weekends, which he did, because he went to bed in the afternoon on Saturdays and Sundays to recover.

We found a tutor who came every Saturday morning for three hours, but Ricky began to fall asleep at the table. We decided he should be left to sleep in in the morning and have his tutoring in the afternoon, but even that didn't work for more than a week or two. Peter Bentley, the tutor, told us we were wasting our money and his time.

'He seems incapable of concentrating. He can't take anything in. Do you think he's quite all right? I mean, is he unwell? Perhaps he should see a doctor. But until he is more, how shall I put it, *compos mentis*, there is little point in my carrying on.'

I was shaken and decided to take Ricky to the doctor and have him checked out. Ricky came extremely reluctantly and told the doctor that he was just tired and he didn't know why, nor what all the fuss was about. Dr Browning looked at him without commenting and took his pulse and then leant over and lifted Ricky's eyelid.

'I think we'll do a blood test, just to see if you're low on iron,' he suggested. 'Your eyes are quite bloodshot and your pulse is a little lower than it should be. How much do you drink?'

Ricky flushed and said, 'Not that much. No more than my friends.'

'And how much is that?' inquired Dr Browning.

'Oh, I dunno. A few pints, I guess.'

'And is that every night, or only at the weekends?'

Ricky wriggled on the seat, and leaning forward, pushed his hands through his hair, staring at the floor.

'Most nights, I guess.'

'Well lad, that's far too much alcohol for anyone, let alone someone of your age. You must keep your drinking to the weekends, and only one or two pints even then, at the most. And what about drugs? Do you smoke pot? I'm afraid I have to ask this in front of your aunt as you're not eighteen, and she's your legal guardian while your parents are abroad.'

I was astonished at Dr Browning's directness as it had never occurred to me that Ricky would be smoking pot. I held my breath and waited for him to answer.

'Sometimes.'

63

'And how often is sometimes?'

'I dunno. At the weekends mostly, I suppose,' Ricky answered belligerently.

My heart was a tight ball of anxiety. I remembered Jane's suspicions about drugs. I didn't know this Ricky, and I didn't know how to deal with it. Drink and drugs! No wonder he was falling asleep all the time! I wondered if that was what the tutor had implied when he asked if Ricky was all right. I was feeling increasingly anxious and out of my depth.

'Well you'd better lay off that, too. It's against the law and anyway it will kill off your brain cells, which I'm sure you know.' Turning to me, he said 'I'll arrange for the nurse to take a blood sample, Mrs Wilton, and I'll call you as soon as we have the results. But this young man must curb his habits immediately, before he becomes addicted.'

We drove home in silence. I didn't know what to say. Eventually, unable to bear the silence any longer, I patted his hand and said 'you're going to be fine darling, we'll help you. I'm sure it's just a bad patch. You'll get over it, I know you will.' Ricky didn't answer and stared at his chewed finger nails the whole way home, and as soon as we had opened the front door, he went straight to his room and locked the door.

I told Tommy about the visit to the doctor that evening, while Ricky was still in his room.

'He doesn't drink in front of us,' Tommy said, 'so I suppose it can't be that bad. But what is he smoking?'

'Dope, he said.'

'Well we smoked plenty of dope when we were young, didn't we? And we're all right, so perhaps we shouldn't worry too much.'

'But what about what his tutor said? He won't come back if Ricky sleeps through every session.'

'Perhaps we should give the lad the benefit of the doubt for the moment. After all he's been through a great deal and is very angry with both his parents. Do you think we should contact Billy and ask him to step in for a while? It might help. He's still the boy's father and should take some responsibility.'

'Oh *Tommy*! You know how he feels about his father! I think Billy is the last person on *earth* Ricky would want to help him out. He despised the way Billy fell apart after Ruth left, and then he abandoned them too. It's because of his parents he's in this mess in the first place.'

'No Maisie! It's because of his *mother*! Billy had nothing to do with her leaving, you know that, and he was equally devastated by her silence. Why should he take the blame? As a man I am completely on his side. I feel he's been extremely badly treated by his wife. All that rubbish about falling in love and then discarding him like an empty beer can in a two line note! For God's sake! You just don't run away from your responsibilities on teenage emotions! It's nothing but pure selfishness. She's his *mother*! And wherever she is, she didn't even send him a birthday card. What kind of mother is that? I never understood Ruth, and I never will!'

Sorry, Ruth, but that's the way he felt, and there seems no point in hiding it from you. And as you will see, I did tell Tommy about Fernando. But only Tommy, no one else, I assure you.

So we struggled on and although we gave up the tutor, Ricky managed to get himself up most mornings and went to school for the day. Only now do I appreciate what a superhuman effort

65

it was for him to do that, but it didn't last long. It was unsustainable and he crashed.

The first sign of the depth of his alcoholism came over New Year. Ricky went out with Alec to a club and Alec came home at 1 a.m. as we had agreed, but Ricky stayed out all night and didn't come back for three days. When he did return he looked like death warmed up, and was filthy dirty and stank of vomit. He almost fell through the front door, and I cried with anger and relief at seeing him home. Of course I didn't get a chance to let off steam and tell him just what I thought of him, as he rushed upstairs and locked the door to his bedroom, and I think he must have slept solidly for eighteen hours, because we didn't hear a single movement from his room the entire time. When he did emerge, he was shamefaced and sheepish, but also dismissive.

'Sorry, Maisie and Tommy. Been on a bit of a bender, good old Tyneside New Year, you know!' He tried to laugh it off, but I didn't find it funny.

'Where the hell have you been these last three days?' I asked angrily.

'Just around with mates.'

'And what about food and somewhere to sleep?'

'Sort of hand to mouth, really. But it was fine and I'm fine, so please don't *fuss*, Maisie.'

'If you're going to live under our roof, you'd better mend your ways and live by the house rules,' Tommy told him. 'You have a mobile, don't you? Well damn well use it lad, and at least have the decency to let us know you're O.K. Your aunt and I have driven all over the countryside looking for you, and it was *not* how we would choose to start the New Year. An apology would be nice, if that's not too much to ask?'

66

Tommy is never sarcastic, but, like me, he had been driven mad with anxiety and we had, as he said, spent days scouring Tyneside for Ricky. Rightly or wrongly, we decided not to go to the police. We thought that if he were found with drugs on him he would be in very serious trouble and so we searched high and low for him ourselves, in the hope of finding him before the police did. I had phoned every one of his friends whose number I knew, but no one could tell us where he was. We were as nervous as kittens and jumped every time the telephone rang. We didn't tell Jane for the first twenty-four hours, but we had to in the end. She was frantic and had also heard nothing from Ricky. The whole world seemed to be searching for him and yet, there he sat, without a glimmer of remorse. We were incensed.

'If you're going to attack me, I might as well leave now,' he said.

We were open mouthed in astonishment.

'How dare you speak to us like that, Ricky? We've done our best to help you, and is this all the thanks we get?' retorted Tommy.

'Look, I'm sorry, O.K.? Now can we forget about it? I'm starving, what's for dinner?'

'I haven't even given it a thought,' I answered icily. 'We've been too busy searching for you. We haven't slept for three nights worrying about you, Ricky. Don't you feel *any* remorse?' And do you know what he answered? 'Join the club!' And he laughed and went to have a bath.

A few weeks later my Minister from church came round for a drink and to talk about a fund-raising event he was planning. I went to pour him a sherry and although the bottle was still in the cupboard, it was empty. I offered him a whisky, but that bottle was empty too, and so were the bottles of gin and vodka.

'I'm so sorry, George! We must have used up our small supply over Christmas, and I'm afraid the cupboard is bare. Would a cup of coffee be acceptable instead?'

I knew instantly who had drunk all the alcohol, and I couldn't concentrate on anything George said. After a little while he asked, 'Is everything all right, Maisie? You seem rather preoccupied?'

'Sorry, George. I've been worrying about my mother, and my mind is rather taken up with her,' I lied.

'Anything I can do?'

'Not really...it's so kind of you to ask. Just pray for her, please.'

'I'll certainly do that. Shall we call it a day, then, and I'll get cracking with our plans?'

'Thank you. Yes. And please forgive my distraction.'

Tommy kept a few bottles of wine under the stairs for Christmas and special occasions, and as soon as I had shut the door behind my Minister, I hurried to see if they were still there. Of course they were not, and I slumped down outside the cupboard and put my head in my hands. Ricky had obviously been helping himself to our drink until it ran out, and I wondered what he would do now. Perhaps if I refilled the wine cupboard and the drinks cabinet, and didn't mention it, he would not feel guilty and it would just blow over? He probably wasn't drinking now that we had run out, I thought, and so it was safe to cover up for him, and give him a little support. Turn a blind eye. I knew almost nothing about alcoholism in those days, and have since learnt that covering up for Ricky made me what is called his 'enabler'. It was probably the worst thing I could have done, but as I

68

was entirely ignorant of the disease, I restocked both the drinks cabinet and the wine store. Another thing about addicts is that they become extremely adept manipulators and liars. After I had refilled the drinks store for the third time in almost as many weeks, Ricky came to me when we were alone and put his arms around me so sweetly, and said, 'Thanks for the drinks, Maisie. It stops me from going out too long in the evening. Much appreciated.' Of course I didn't know that he was selling the wine and spirits to buy skunk and drinking the whisky himself. It was also costing me a fortune, but I was happy to do it if it meant that Ricky came home every night. I felt I had some control if I could at least see him before he went to school and in the evening over dinner, so we carried on this charade for a few weeks, until the headmaster rang again.

'Mrs Wilton? Good morning, Philip Adams here. I'll come straight to the point if you don't mind. I'm afraid I have bad news. We've pushed the boat out to the limit and can no longer keep Ricky at St Gregory's. As he's hardly been here since the New Year, I'm sure it will come as no surprise to you. It wasn't for the lack of trying from our end, I assure you. I'm very sorry, very sorry indeed, as I hate to be defeated, but that's what we are. Utterly defeated. It's such a shame, that boy had so much going for him and he's thrown it all away. I just hope he doesn't live to regret it. Perhaps he'll come round one day; one can only hope. But a lad with such an apparent disregard for his own health and safety often ends up in big trouble. I just hope he can get a grip on himself in time.'

I slid to the floor in a crumpled heap and closed my eyes, cradling the telephone against my ear, listening, but not wanting to hear another word.

69

'But what will become of my nephew?' I asked at last. I knew I sounded pathetic.

'It's really up to him to pull himself together. He should get a job straight away. He's a bright lad, so I hope he'll find one, and we can only hope that he will realise that his long term opportunities will be vastly improved by taking his A levels and getting a good degree. Over to you now, I'm afraid. Good luck. I wish you, and him, all the best.'

I was too ashamed to tell Mr Adams that I had thought Ricky had been going to school all along. I felt stupid and embarrassed and utterly at a loss. There was nothing more to be said, so I thanked Mr Adams for all his efforts and said goodbye. Little did I know that this was just the beginning of our troubles.

I will have to finish here, Ruth. I'm sorry to leave you with an open-ended email, but it is already very long, and I'm so tired from reliving it through writing it all down. I hope you'll understand and I will write more once I have regained my equilibrium.

With love,

Maisie

From: Ruth Braydon ruthbraydon@cedaw.com.ar
Date: 8th February 2011
To: Maisie Wilton maisiewilton@btinternet.com

Dear Maisie,

I don't know what to say. What on earth do you mean, "this was just the beginning of our troubles"? Isn't his dependence on alcohol and dope enough? My poor sister - and Tommy. And my brave daughter! Please, please continue as soon as possible, I can't bear the gaps between our emails; the agony of waiting each day in hope of news is torture. Although of course I do shoulder *some* responsibility, even though I left Jane and Ricky well provided for, *and* with their father. And he was *fine* when I left. He was 100% *fine*.

My immediate reaction was to pick up the phone and speak to you. But as my hand reached out to dial your number, I realised that painful news cannot be spurted out just like that, and that one needs time, and peace and quiet to collect one's thoughts before writing them down. And I *do* realise having to tell me blow by blow must be incredibly difficult for you. So *thank you* for all the writing. Thank you for your *enormous courage* in reliving the nightmare so that I, whom you consider was the main cause of Ricky's addiction, could know. So I will be patient Maisie, but I beg you not to hold out for a second longer than is necessary.

I also acknowledge that any anguish and turmoil I am feeling is no doubt insignificant compared to what you and Tommy have suffered, had to live through and deal with, but I am asking you, no, I am *pleading* with you, to write as soon as possible. It will be very distressing to read of our mother's sad, final years, but it pales to a shadow when compared to one so young. After all, Mum was 84 when she died, and Ricky still has his whole life ahead of him. My son, an alcoholic! I wouldn't have known what to do. I still don't. Drugs and alcoholism are entirely outside my field of experience. And yours, too, as you have said. Oh God, Maisie!

I am at your mercy, Maisie, as you were at mine in our childhood. Be kinder to me than I ever was to you, if you can.

And what was happening to Mum while all this was going on? With much love,

Ruth

From: Maisie Wilton maisiewilton@btinternet.com
Date: 10th February 2011
To: Ruth Braydon ruthbraydon@cedaw.com.ar

Dear Ruth,

I'm sorry that my last email caused you so much pain. I did warn you but I didn't know how else to tell you except to write it down exactly as it happened. If I am to give you the whole picture it will take time, and now you have some idea why. As you so rightly said, these things cannot be spurted out, just like that. I need to gather my thoughts, and remember each event as it happened. So be patient with me, and I will do my best to tell you everything. He is all right *now*. That's all that matters, in the long run, wouldn't you agree? So if you still want chapter and verse, I will tell you, but in my own time, if you can bear it. After all, there is no rush, is there, if you know it all ends well?

For the moment, I will return to what happened to Mum, since you asked, and what was happening to us all while we were looking after Ricky. And perhaps in the telling you will understand family matters that I learned after you had left home, but it will require some background. And as Mum only died three months ago, she is still very much on my mind. Her last week and death are still fresh and painful to me.

As you know, both Tommy and I love children and Tommy spent his life working at a local school for disabled teenagers. That was where we met after all, when I was working as a Special Needs Teacher with Class 10 and Tommy was the Deputy Head. He had already been at Saint Bede's for years and I was new, almost straight out of college, and terrified. I don't know if you remember what a nervous wreck I was in those days? I had just finished my training and was 21 and living in a flat in Jesmond, away from home for the first time. I couldn't afford to live with students while I was training, although I would have loved to have done so. Dad was reluctant enough to pay for me to go to college, and he "certainly wasn't going to throw good money after bad, just so I could stay out all night and not get found out" as he used to say. It was Mum who fought my corner, not, I am ashamed to admit, me, to get him to agree first for me to stay on at school and take A levels, and then go to college. The rows they had! It was awful, Ruth. You had already left home, but I didn't have the bottle. I also felt there was only me left to stand between him and Mum, but of course that was all nonsense. No one stood between them, no one ever stood up to Dad and lived, except Mum. Or continued to live under the same roof. Look what happened to you and Mike. I stayed because I suppose I didn't have the guts or the money to leave. I also stayed to keep Mum company after you two had gone. Not that I want to make you feel bad about that. It was my own choice which I had made freely, just as you both made yours. But the last one left has to hold the baby so to speak, and that last one was me.

Dad was going through a particularly bad few years at that time. The building trade was changing dramatically to suit the times, and Dad didn't understand the new way. He hated everything the 1960's symbolised, the pill, emancipation of wo-men, Flower Power and particularly 'lefty politics' as he called it. People wanted modern homes and craftsmanship was rapidly becoming a dying art. They no longer wanted oak and stone, but stripped pine and steel and fitted kitchens and cupboards every-where. Lovely family homes were carved into tiny flats by cowboy builders and he was left with a large amount of unsold stock. He was out of his element and out of fashion. It created problems at work and his profits fell, but not by half as much as he would have liked us to believe. He refused to listen to Gordon, his foreman, whose opinion he had valued for thirty years and this caused daily friction between them. He was always angry, forever at the point of exploding, like a pressure cooker with the lid screwed on too tightly. Mum found respite in work and thank goodness had her office to escape to, but home life was extremely difficult. We learned not to say anything that might arouse him, and clung together in our silence like two people alone on a shipwreck knowing that no one could save us but ourselves, and our sheer will to survive. At times it felt as if the house were a satellite Chinese gulag, living in constant fear of enraging the camp guard, our real opinions and the truth hidden in the depths of our hearts. Perhaps you think I am being overly dramatic, but it was so, Ruth, nevertheless.

Dad behaved appallingly when Mike said he wanted to go to university. That was in the middle of those long, hard years.

"What the *hell* do you want to do that for?" he'd yell at Mike. "Haven't I spent enough on your education already? You've got more 'O' levels than any human can possibly need, and in useless subjects like Greek and Latin, for God's sake, and now you do nothing but witter on about how Mr Twit and Mr Twat say how clever you are, filling your stupid head with ideas about this *university* business." He used to say 'university' with sneering emphasis and an expression that conveyed that the very word 'university' smelt like dog shit to him.

"I've done very well with no education. And I'll remind you yet again, that everything you see in this room, including the nice house you have had the luxury of living in for free for the past 17 years, has all been earned by the sweat from my own brow. Without any unnecessary *university* education. You're getting too big for your boots, my lad. Learn a useful trade and *work*. That's all there is too it, just *hard work and determination*. Get it? I will *never* pay for *university*."

And he never did. It took all Mum's gentle persuasion over years to persuade him that we were bright children which was a great blessing and that we should stay at school until we had taken A levels. Dad had expected we would leave at sixteen, which was all the education anyone could possibly need for a full working life he believed, any more being mere intellectual vanity. She began when we were still at primary school, as soon as she was sure we were above average and it was not just childhood precocity that would fade and disappear like the stars at dawn, once we became teenagers. She knew what she had produced and delighted in our achievements and abilities, but it was Mike's *height* that pushed Dad over the edge. Crazy I know, but Mike agrees with me. When he started to shoot up as fast as Jack's beanstalk, overtaking Dad by a good two inches, he resented Mike for *just being taller than him!* It was something that for the first time in Mike's life Dad could not control and I think he found shouting *up* at Mike humiliating. When Mike was sixteen and had reached six feet making him a full four inches taller than Dad, Dad reacted as if he had grown out of sheer insolence, and that was when he began making caustic comments about how much Mike ate and how expensive he was to feed and clothe. When Mike was over during Mum's last few days, we talked about it again and both came to the same conclusion. Mike said Dad had a heavy dose of 'small man syndrome,' a well known and well researched phenomenon. But I don't think it was only Mike's height that made Dad difficult, it was our education more than anything. We began to know more than he did and it made him feel extremely uncomfortable; and so he reacted with aggression instead of pride. That's why he never discussed history, science or literature, only sport and current affairs and business, of course. It was a direct result of his background, and although he worshipped Mum, he could never come to terms with the fact that she came from an educated family while his was working class.

Often, when Dad was watching football or sport on television, Mum and I would go and sit quietly together in her cosy study and talk about his childhood. I understood, even though she never actually said so, that she wanted to excuse him, to make me feel less resentful towards him and his behaviour to us, and to Mike in particular. Although I have always loved to hear family history, and enjoyed our evenings together, it didn't change my opinion of him one iota. Throughout her life, come hell or high water, Mum was always kind and forgiving towards him. She was a saint. But actually, I think it was much simpler than that. She just loved him and knew what he was and where he had come from and how he had struggled, so she forgave him everything, although it never stopped her from fighting our corner. But the point I must make very clear here, is that she fought him *for* us, never against *him*, as a man. See the difference? And I'm not excusing him Ruth, although I know you'll think I am. Or just being weak again. Tommy and I always saw forgiveness as man's greatest strength and it is a universal virtue in every religion, I think you would agree. And understanding is the first step towards it, so I suppose that that is why Mum told me many family stories during those difficult years, to engender understanding and forgiveness for our father, rather than hatred and resentment.

She told me that Grandpa and Grandma Campbell had had a terrible struggle to keep their family going during the 1920's and 1930's. Grandpa Campbell had diabetes and medicines were very expensive - it was long before the creation of the National Health. Sometimes nearly all his weekly earnings had to be spent on medication and Dad had had to work after school every day and all weekend to make up the deficit. As he was the eldest of four children, he was thrown into responsibility at a very young age. When Grandpa was too ill to go to work, Dad would take his place at the mill instead of going to school. The men at the mill were wonderful to him, never saying a word, just quietly helping him out if he were not strong or fast enough to run several machines at a time. But the foreman was not so kind, and at every opportunity would upbraid Dad for having a "weakling for a father" which Dad resented bitterly, but he did at least let him take Grandpa's place. Sometimes Grandpa would be sick for weeks at a time and then the foreman would tell Dad that although he wanted to help the family out, Dad was under age and if the owner of the mill found out that Dad was filling his father's place, it would mean that he, the foreman, would get the sack. Talk about pressure! And Dad was short, just like his parents, and although he tried hard to grow a beard to appear older than his years, he could only produce a bit of blond fluff, and that annoyed him too. Luckily, as Dad had been christened Douglas after Grandpa, the weekly pay cheque did not present any difficulty.

As soon as his sister and brothers were old enough they left school and took whatever work they could find. Aunty Lyn went to work in a clothing factory sewing buttons on coats for ten hours a day for almost nothing, which eventually wrecked her eye sight. And the two boys, Uncle Jimmy and Uncle Bert, both went to the dockyard as soon as they could and were hired by Swan Hunter, the famous ship builder; where they worked all their lives apart from during the war, when they naturally fought in the Navy. Dad finally gave up any thought of school at fourteen. He had been able to go less and less frequently as Grandpa's diabetes became increasingly debilitating, and so he left and went to work for Mr Wandsworth at Wandsworth Construction in Wallsend, near his brothers at Swan Hunter. And that was where he learnt the building trade.

His "rise to prosperity" as he liked to call it, was the day that Danny O'Doyle fell and broke his leg. Dad had been working under Danny O'Doyle for a couple of years, and Danny loved Dad. His called him "his little right hand lad" which gave Dad pride while at the same time he deeply resented any reference to his short stature. Danny O'Doyle's only son had died from measles on his fifth birthday, which had broken Danny's heart, and he called Dad "his second son" and taught him everything he knew. Dad was clever, a quick learner and an extremely hard worker. He never said he couldn't do something and he never complained of being tired, although it was gruellingly hard work and very long hours. He never took a day off even if he was sick, and once kept going even after he had dislocated his shoulder, until he eventually passed out with pain. Danny O'Doyle was terribly upset that he hadn't noticed, and immediately sent Dad to the local doctor who put his shoulder back and insisted that he took the rest of the day off! Dad was back at work the following morning, white faced and uncomplaining, but that shoulder gave him grief for the rest of his life. He has arthritis in it now but needless

79

to say, won't take anything for it; he just becomes even more bad tempered on the days when it is particularly painful.

The day Danny O'Doyle broke his leg Dad carried him to the doctor, even though Danny was a big man, and at least 13 stone. Danny had slipped on a broken rung and had fallen backwards down the ladder while carrying a hod of bricks over his shoulder. Fortunately for him, only one of the bricks shook lose, but it fell diagonally across his shin and shattered the bone. The foreman watched as Dad staggered across the yard with Danny in his arms yelling blue murder, and began to notice him. He realised what a good worker Dad was and when he began to talk to him, discovered he had an innate intelligence. He asked Dad to work for him while Danny was off sick and during that time put Dad through his paces. First he set him to work in the accounts department, and although Dad had had little formal education, numbers came to him instinctively. The simplicity of numbers pleased him. He loved their stability, their uncomplicated straightforwardness. There could be no argument with mathematics; it was either right or wrong. The foreman, Mr Cartwright, showed Dad how to quantify all building materials, how many bricks were needed per square foot and what different types of bricks there were and which bricks were best suited to different buildings. He then set Dad to work in plumbing, followed by metal work, then electricity cabling and so, in this way, he learned all about the different types of materials used in building work, and how much was needed for each job, and how much to order. He worked quietly in the office, fascinated with the subject, enjoying using his brain although, he said, on sunny days he missed being outside in the fresh air and working alongside the other men. But the men in the office were wary of him. He was young and had become Mr Cartwright's "blue eyed boy", so they didn't speak to him much. Not that Dad cared. He was immersed in learning the 'real trade' as he called it. Profit. How it was made and lost. A lesson that he never forgot, and it became his God, his saviour, and through profit, he hoped he would be able to save his family from destitution.

Six months later, even though Danny had been back at work as soon as his leg could bear his weight, Dad was still under Mr Cartwright's wing. Arthur Cartwright was an astute manager and recognised a keen mind and fierce ambition when it presented itself to him. Wandsworth Construction had just won a contract to build a new housing estate in County Durham. There had been fierce competition for the contract and the houses were bound to sell like hot cakes as the demand for good new housing after the war had not lessened. New housing estates and whole new towns continued to spring up all over the country, such as Peterlee. They were nice, but remember all those ghastly tower blocks that were built in the 1960's? Of course we now know that the old back-to-back houses with the lanes running between them supported whole communities, which were destroyed when families moved into tower blocks.

Mr Wandsworth gave Arthur Cartwright the new estate to build, and that night he took Dad to the pub and bought him a pint to celebrate.

'I want you with me, Douglas,' he said. 'You've proved yourself to me many times over the past six months and this is your opportunity to really forge ahead. What do you say? Of course, it'll be a hard graft. If you think you've been working hard up till now lad, why, that was as good as sleepwalking. I'm talking tough, really tough; do you think you can handle it? After all, you're not built like a tank are ye?'

That was all Dad needed, a goad to his manpower, his strength and his stature, and he rose to the bait.

'Of course I'm up to it, Mr Cartwright!' he exclaimed, almost rising from his seat in heat.

'Steady on, lad!' Arthur had replied. 'I just want you to know what you're in for, that's all.'

'I know a golden opportunity when I see one,' Dad had answered. 'When do we start?'

'These things take a bit of time, son. But if I know my boss, it won't be as long as most. He'll seal the contract this week and we'll begin the next!' They raised their glasses and Dad, believe it not, apparently sang at the top of his flat voice all the way home.

Mum said that was the beginning of Dad's real economic rise. The building project was 'a miracle', according to the press. It was built in under the estimated time and all the houses were sold before completion.

I'm tired now, Ruth and must go to bed. I seem to have gone way off the point, but there is so much to say and so much history to cover. There's a great deal I feel I should write to you about our family and what happened, and each time I try to write about Mum and her passing, our family history seems to take over and demand to be told first. I can't explain it, it just happens while I sit at my computer. I hope you can bear with me. I have never been one for protracted tales, but this seems to be outside my control. I'll continue later. Till then, goodnight, and sweet dreams.

Love,

Maisie

From: Ruth Braydon ruthbraydon@cedaw.com.ar
Date: 12th February 2011
To: Maisie Wilton maisiewilton@btinternet.com

Dear Maisie,

Reading about Dad's background made his behaviour a *little* more understandable. For instance, I didn't know the full story of his childhood nor about his "rise to prosperity", but I was never as interested in our family history as you were; Mike and I just wanted out! And of course you had to stay at home much longer that either of us. I can see why he was so kind to his own family. It was probably because of his upbringing that made him so determined and unreasonably strict with us. They had had such a tough life and he didn't want us to be spoilt, but to build our own lives as he had had to do, and he no doubt felt that he had given us a good start. But he was so irrational and heavy handed about it. *And* I feel compelled to say that although it was a touching story, it didn't change my view of him as a man, except to honour his achievements; as you say, it didn't change yours either. Because where is the value in material achievements if one remains a cruel and overbearing person? We would all far rather have had a father who was less high achieving and more generous of heart and spirit. I can imagine how the house became a "Chinese gulag" as you so descriptively put it. Poor you.

When I escaped from home at seventeen, Mike had not even taken his O levels and you were only a very young thirteen year old. I came home as little as I could, as you'll probably recall, as each visit inevitably culminated in another ugly row. I tried to keep my voice down and my temper under control not to upset you, but it is not in my nature to be conciliatory, and you were so easily upset and hated rows. I couldn't bear Mum's compliance with Dad; it drove me to distraction. And it seemed out of character for her, as well as entirely unnecessary. Mum was well educated and extremely well read and I loved being alone with her and talking about life and my exam course work, but whenever we got onto the subject of Dad I always seemed to lose it, causing a painful disagreement, which was hurtful for us both. So it seemed better to get out and stay out, which is what I did. Now I look back, I suppose Mike and I did desert you. It never occurred to us that in saving our own skins, we left you in the lurch. We were too young to realise, and no doubt like all young people, deeply self involved. I am so sorry that you were left alone at home and felt obliged to stay to look after Mum, although I can't imagine that my staying a second longer than I did would have helped you in any way. I was finding Dad insufferable at the time, and it was clear to me that the feeling was mutual. It must have been terrible for our mother, but I had run out of sympathy for her, too.

I had always assumed that Mike had the same problem, which in many ways, he had, but I had no idea the extent of his difficulties with Dad. Imagine Dad being jealous even of his *height*! I knew, we all knew, that Dad had not so much a chip as a veritable *chasm* on his shoulder regarding his lack of education, but to add Mike's height to his irrational behaviour towards him makes me want to question Dad's mental health. Any normal man would have lauded his children's abilities and success, but not our dear father. Oh no, he had to take it as a personal insult that we were better educated than he was. Such insanity! He could no more help his lack of education than we our sharp minds. He was just as bright as any of us, yet he steadfastly refused to expand his narrow horizons, continuing to only have any interest in the building trade, politics and sport. And his politics were so right wing that in my youthful liberalism, I found his views disgusting. In fact, I still do. Studying sociology and Spanish in the '60's was an introduction to left wing views to me, and being a natural fighter, the more I learned of the plight of the poor and the unfairness of our society, the more I turned against our middleclass upbringing and values.

Occasionally Dad would tell to me something of his childhood and the enormous difficulties he and his family had to bear, but his conviction remained that if one didn't get on in life it was entirely due to laziness, and one could not reason with him on the subject. He considered that the lower classes these days had become an ignorant, good-for-nothing lot who fully deserved their self-made misery. He had felt sorry enough for his own family, but had such a blinkered outlook on life that his extremely limited compassion never extended beyond it. What did else did Mike have to say on the subject? I'd love to know, and to have had all the hours you had to talk to him about our childhood. But you did say that Mike left without looking behind him, and so did I.

'You're just like Hitler!' I remember shrieking at Dad during one last, dreadful, unforgettable row. 'You condemn the poor and helpless as nothing but lazy, undeserving riffraff. It's disgusting! They aren't lazy. People can't help being born poor or uneducated. *You* couldn't.'

'No, I could not, nor could my father and mother, but they knew the value of *hard work*, Ruth. These days every lazy blighter is on benefit, while hard working people like me are forced to

support them. *That's* what is disgusting, my girl. And those immigrants are the worst. Stinking drunks, selling God knows what
drugs to our children, living in squalor, and these are the people
you socialists welcome into the country with open arms. "Oh, let
them come in and make themselves at home, let them have hundreds of ugly babies and take up all our state housing so that English people can't even get a home, let alone a decent job. Oh, and
do let's give them plenty of money so they never have to do an
honest day's work", he said in a high, whining voice, screwing his
face into a whinging expression. 'It makes me sick! Why should
I support the lazy buggers? I'd rather give my money to a pikey,
and that's saying something! At least they're white!'

'You're so narrow minded and bigoted. Trying to make out
that the British are a master race. You're no better than Goebbels.
You'd put all the immigrants into a gas chamber if you could!
This country couldn't function without immigrants. Surely even
someone as prejudiced as you can see that?'

'No, I *do not* see that! I've built up my own very successful
company without the need to *ever* employ a single darkie. My
men wouldn't stand for it, and neither would I. Why should I
give jobs to Pakis and blacks when there are plenty of my own
kind who can do the job much better?'

'*Wake up* Dad! Go into any shop or hospital and see who's doing all the work! They certainly aren't your blue eyed boys! None
of "your own kind" wants to do that kind of work any more.'

'Now listen here, you' he said, leaning so far over me that I
could not have bent backwards any further, and prodding me in
the chest with his fat forefinger. 'I've heard just about enough
of your stupid, lefty clap-trap. You're just a bolshie little twit
whose mouth is much too big for her small head. You haven't the

86

faintest idea what you're talking about. You make me sick with it. But you're happy enough to live off my back though, aren't you? So why don't you stand on your own two feet, Ruth, and tell me how you like it. You can start off standing in a queue at the Job Centre *behind* all your darkie friends and tell me then how much you like them taking your job and house from under your own stupid nose!'

'Believe me, I'd move out of here in a second, if I could. But d'you know what, Dad? I'm working hard for my exams to get into university and if I could afford to work to pay rent as well as study, I'd be out of here like a shot! I can't wait to leave this place!'

'You see? You stupid idiot! You've already given in! You'd rather lose your loud mouthed principals and live off my hard work than actually put your money where your mouth is. You'd rather stay *here,* where you're warm, housed and fed, all bills paid by *me,* your "bigoted father", than give up school and go out to work to prove your point. Actions speak louder than words my girl, so don't you *ever dare* to talk to me like that again, because if you do, I'll *throw you* out, whether you like it or not!'

Horrendous as it was, that particular argument did cause me to pause and reflect, Maisie. Because his last point was right, although I would have died rather than admit it. I didn't leave home until I had taken my A levels and so I did take the easy option. But how I suffered for it until I left home! I was unable to disagree with him again after that because I was genuinely afraid that he would throw me out, whatever Mum said. And I couldn't face living in some filthy bedsit and studying every night all alone, so I did have to shut up for at least six months until I had finished. And although I had to work my way through university, because of course, as you'll remember, he refused to pay for me, too, I was never quite as hard up as Mike, because I began earning after three years, whereas it took Mike six years to qualify to be a doctor. And Dad did occasionally help me out, like buying me that beaten up old post office van which I adored.

It also made life a little easier at home when we stopped rowing. I could see your little pinched face brighten and begin to relax, which made me feel really bad. Your shoulders used to rise up to your ears at mealtimes, were you aware of that? Dreading any conversation turning to something that would cause a fight between Dad and me. You looked so tiny and scared and tense, Maisie. And so vulnerable. I really *did* try to control myself for your benefit, but it was almost impossible at times.

Anyway, 'qui s'explique, s'accuse,' as the French say. Please write again soon, and don't take offence, Maisie. There's been too much of that in our past and we don't need it. Older, wiser, and all that!

And if you think forgiveness is man's greatest strength, I'm asking you to practice it on me!

Your loving {Bolshie!} sister,

Ruth

From: Maisie Wilton maisiewilton@btinternet.com
Date: 16th February 2011
To: Ruth Braydon ruthbraydon@cedaw.com.ar

Dear Ruth,

It's very interesting to hear your side of the story at last. How I hated all that rowing! And to think that I was being sheltered from the worst excesses! Thank you, Ruth, for that.

I'll return to Mum as I seem to be continuously blown off track and down various memory lanes each time I write to you. I'll try my best to stick to her story and digress as little as possible. But it is hard after so long because one story leads to another and then another and before I realise I have written volumes of childhood memories and am still way behind telling you about Mum and your own family. So here goes:

After she had the three pins to secure her hip, she slowly recovered and for a while life returned to normal, except she had to give up work as she found she just didn't have what she always referred to as her 'energy force' any more. She could manage their everyday lives, but working full-time at interior design was impossible. Looking back, it was amazing that she had continued for so long; she was already 78 when she broke her hip. Of course she couldn't resist helping people out whenever they asked her, which they did often. Her friend Barbara was always popping in with some design problem or another in one of her boutique hotels, asking Mum for advice about colours and fabrics and bringing carrier bags full of samples to show her, afraid to make a decision without first securing Mum's approval. But once she had put Barbara on the right path, the conversation turned to Barbara's personal life, her aging parents and her difficult children in particular. This always took another two hours at least, but Mum sat and listened, as she always did, giving her full attention, ensuring that the listener, whoever it was, because there were many others apart from Barbara, felt that they had her undivided attention and all the hours God gave to devote herself to whoever it was who needed her calm, non-judgmental wisdom. It was her unique gift, listening, and she gave each visitor her whole heart. Just as she did when their old friend, Jimmy Earle, was sent down for stealing cash from children's charities. She never criticised him or blamed him, she just listened and offered love and sympathy. That was all he wanted, a kind heart and undivided attention. That's really all any of us want isn't it? Just a bit of kindness and understanding. Life is surprisingly simple when you strip it back to the essentials. Jimmy had had judge and jury aplenty and had to face his own demons every day, but Mum gave him comfort and sandwiches without judgement, and so he came every Friday evening as regular as clockwork, until he was sent down for eighteen months, and then again, every Friday evening, once he had been released.

She even went to visit him in prison. At least a couple of times of which I am aware. I thought it was very brave of her and he was so pathetically grateful, she told me, it was enough to break her heart. Dad didn't go, of course. He just called Jimmy 'a stupid idiot and a gambler' because that was the reason he stole, to feed his gambling habit. But until the day he died he never admitted to any fault. Mum used to say, "No one in prison ever admits his guilt. Every prisoner protests his innocence, and who am I to judge?" That was her way and Tommy and I thought it was beautiful.

One morning around that time, when I popped in on my way to the supermarket to ask if I could pick up anything for her, she asked me to come upstairs to her bedroom. It was early, and she had just come out of the shower and was still in her dressing gown.

'Now Maisie, I don't want to frighten you, but I have had this lump under my breast for some time, and as you are here while I am still undressed, I wonder if you'd have a look at it, darling?'

She took off her dressing gown and as naked as a babe, lifted her breast and let me feel the lump under the outer side of her right breast. It was quite a large lump Ruth, about the size of a broad bean, and even I, a layman, could not mistake it, so I asked her how long she had had it.

'I don't really know Maisie, but quite some time, I think.'

'Why didn't you tell me sooner, Mum?' I asked.

'I was hoping that it would just go away,' she answered quietly. And when I looked at her, it was like looking at a child who had just discovered a body in the yard, and was very frightened.

'I think we should ask a doctor, Mum. It's probably nothing more than a fatty lump, but it's best to check, don't you think?' I was shaken Ruth, that's the truth, but of course I didn't want to upset her.

'All right then Maisie, if you think so. Perhaps you would make me an appointment at the hospital, but don't please don't tell Dad. It'll only worry him.'

So I dropped in on her GP who suggested I take Mum for a test at the R.V.I.

It was a lovely spring morning in April about three years ago now, and as we drove through Newcastle we admired the daffodils and the emerging tulips and both commented on how

much we loved this time of year. Lovely spring, symbolic of re-
newed hope, and every year we felt the same surge rising in tune
to the sap in the trees. Hope for a wonderful summer to come
and to our lives in general. I've always felt that hope was far greater than love, despite St. Paul's conviction that love conquers all.
Rubbish! Hope wins every time, don't you agree? How can one
live without it? It is hope alone that has got me through my
darkest hours. It is hope that gives me the strength to go on,
not love! "Love is for pansies," as Dad would say, "not for real
men" and I agree with him when it refers to romantic love, which
is never more than tenuous, but much less so when it is deep,
abiding love. But nevertheless, hope still seems to me to be the
stronger of the two.

Anyway {apologies, I've digressed again}, there we were in my
little car admiring the spring and full of optimism until we were
in the consulting room of Mr Spencer, the breast specialist. He
was sweet and gentle with Mum, and while he was examining her
he took a close look at her face and said quite simply, 'You seem
to be in the early stages of Parkinson's disease, Mrs Campbell.
Have you found that you have a problem with pencil control recently?'

Mum looked up at him, her baby blue eyes welling with tears
of fear.

'Yes, now you mention it I have, doctor,' she replied, so quietly
that I don't think he would have heard her if he hadn't been
bending over her.

'I have found typing on the lovely new laptop my son bought
me quite difficult recently. But I assumed it was just my age. I
used to run my own business so I have always done a lot of typ-

ing, but recently the words seem to join up and I have lost my speed.'

'That's a sure sign,' he answered, as if he were talking about nothing more than the coming of winter and the inevitable dying off of garden annuals. 'I suggest you make an appointment to see Mr Smythe. He also works at the RVI and is a specialist in Parkinson's disease. He'll diagnose you quickly enough, but I can tell you now that's what you've got. I can see it in your face, just here,' he said, waving his hand vaguely over her cheek, as if he were indicating a mild rash, not the signs of an incurable, crippling disease. 'As for your breast cancer,' he continued, seemingly completely unaware how he was imparting devastating news as casually as if he were warning us about heavy traffic on the way home, as if cancer could be as easily avoided, 'at your age it will be very slow growing and is really nothing to worry about. I'll prescribe you some pills which will both slow the growth and soften the lump. And please don't worry, Mrs Campbell, at your age, old age will take you long before breast cancer!' At that point he mentally dismissed Mum and honestly Ruth, I really believe that if she had been a horse, he would have discharged her with a comforting pat on the rump.

We staggered outside into the bright spring light but before we could reach the car we both stopped in shock, quite unable to move, and I took her in my arms and found myself muttering into her stunned and deafened ears, just how much I loved her. It was an awful moment, and one I will take to my grave. Mum seemed to have had all her strength squeezed from her in that one sentence. She had visibly crumpled like a fragile paper bag that had been viciously crushed by a large, firm hand.

'Oh, Maisie!' was all she could say as she leant against me.

I held her and hugged her and we both cried like babies, tears rolling down our cheeks as freely as water from a tap. I didn't know what to say but found myself muttering 'You'll be all right. I'll be with you. There are wonderful drugs for these things nowadays,' knowing how trite I sounded. But I didn't know what else to do. Mum and Dad had had several friends who had had Parkinson's and there was no hiding the awful truth from her. We both had visions of her unable to walk, to take herself to the loo, to dress and put on her makeup. She had always been such an immaculate, private person in those matters.

Somehow, God alone knows how, we reached the car and drove home in shocked silence. We had only been to visit the specialist about an innocent fatty lump in her breast and had left in the full knowledge that she suddenly had both breast cancer and Parkinson's disease. It made her broken hip seem like a summer dance in comparison.

I can't remember much of what happened after I got her home. I vaguely remember putting the kettle on and making us a cup of tea. Dad was out and we sat in silence and sipped our tea, staring into space, trying to come to terms with her news.

A large blackbird sang noisily in the garden and I resented it daring to be so bold and joyful when we had such devastating news to assimilate. How could it be so insensitive? I imagined myself as a cat, jumping on it and enjoying killing it with my sharp claws, and drinking its warm blood.

After some time we began to talk about what it all meant and how she would cope, and of course, what to tell Dad. Dad was always her first concern, how he would take the news, and how he would manage when she became increasingly infirm. Then I made us a bit of lunch, just a small sandwich, I think, as neither of us had an appetite, and when she had eaten a little, I suggested she had a nap. She followed me upstairs to her bedroom like an obedient child, and I tucked her up and promised to return before Dad came home, and tell him the news myself.

As I drove away from their house, I felt as if I had just said goodbye to her for ever. It was stupid, I know, but life had taken a turn for the worse and would never return to the way it was before, and however bad that might have been, it appeared sweet to me at that moment. I had Radio 3 on in the car but hadn't really been listening until I heard an announcement that the next piece of music was a recording of Renee Fleming singing the final song of Strauss's Four Last Songs. It was by the poet Joseph von Eichendorff called 'At Sunset', which Strauss had set to music, and the final words are "How weary we are of wandering, is this perhaps death?" and is one of my favourite pieces of music. It was both apt and poignant, and it seemed as if I were hearing it for the very first time. Shock and grief can heighten the senses, and tears poured down my face in such a rush that I couldn't see where I was going, and I had to pull onto the hard shoulder with a line of cars behind me hooting angrily. And there I stayed and listened to the magnificent music until the very last note had faded into silence.

When I eventually reached my front door, I had great difficulty in putting the key in the lock. Once inside, I collapsed in a heavy pathetic slump in an armchair in the sitting room, staring into space for I don't know how long, until the kids came home from work and college and I looked up and found them staring at me, looking lost and bewildered. I managed to rally, and drank the cup of tea that Sharon had made for me. She and Alec took Sadie and Joy upstairs and settled them in front of the television in my bedroom before returning to the sitting room to confront me.

'Whatever's going on, Maisie?' Sharon demanded. She was, and still is, a bold girl. 'You look like you've just seen a ghost.' So I told them what had happened that day, but they were still very young, and couldn't grasp the tragic implications.

'Margaret isn't going to die, is she?' Sharon asked directly.

'No, Sharon. But it does mean that life will change rather dramatically for her, and her future isn't at all good,' was all I could muster.

'But what does it really *mean*, Maisie?' she persisted, always the one for getting straight to the point.

'Probably not much, to begin with.'

'Then why the big drama?' she demanded. She didn't mean to be callous; it was just her forceful manner.

'I suppose you're right. But it will mean that Margaret will become increasingly frail and less and less able to do things for herself.'

'That's not so bad at her age, is it?' asked Sharon. 'I mean, she's very old now, isn't she, so getting older and having something wrong with you is sort of normal, isn't it?'

'Yes, it is. But getting older and having Parkinson's disease *and* breast cancer is not usual,' I added, suddenly - God forgive me - feeling irritated by her vigorous youth and easy dismissal of my mother's shocking news.

I should tell you a bit about Sharon, so that you don't think unkindly of her. Tommy and I took her on when she was only eight. She had suffered greatly at the hands of her father and had been left largely on her own to look after her two younger siblings after her English alcoholic mother had died in a car crash.

Her Jamaican father was a violent heroin addict and had abused her often as a child. She felt extremely defensive of her younger sisters and did everything she could to protect them from him. When her father remarried another Jamaican, whose brother decided to join in the abuse, she took her two younger sisters, who were only six and five, and ran away. They were eventually found more than two weeks later, living under a plastic bin bag in Kielder forest, half starved and dangerously dehydrated. The authorities took them into care but Sharon refused them to be separated so, to cut a long story short, Tommy and I took them all in, as our foster children. We already had Alec who was nearly ten at the time, and had been thinking of fostering another child, but when the three of them turned up, looking like starving little blackbirds, it seemed as if it were meant to be. So they all came to live with us, and all three of them stayed with us until each one was old enough to leave home. Sharon still refuses to wear anything that would show the cigarette burns her father scored onto her arms and chest. But despite all their appalling adversities, Dad was always so rude about our "half castes". Enough said, I think. But they have all grown into wonderful people, much more mature at their young age than we were, and a great source of pride to Tommy and me. But it was not, of course, plain sailing. They arrived with an enormous amount of emotional baggage, and it took them a very long time to accept Tommy, Alec and me as their foster family, and for them to learn to trust us.

As I'm sure you are aware, Tommy and I had always wanted a large family. We just assumed that we would have our own family, but try as we might, we were never able to have our own children and we never found out why. "God moves in a mysterious way, His wonders to perform," as William Cowper wrote in his beautiful hymn, and although it wasn't our chosen path to be foster parents, that is how it turned out. If I were young again, I think we would have tried to have our own children through IVF, but IVF hadn't been invented then. I have often considered over the years that perhaps it was the most marvellous thing that happened to us, our inability to conceive, because we were able to help others who were not capable of giving their own children a secure and loving home and those young people gave us so much. Possibly much more than children of our own could have done. Who knows?

So there we are. More another time. My bed calls.

Love, as ever,

Maisie

From: Ruth Braydon ruthbraydon@cedaw.com.ar
Date: 25th February 2011
To: Maisie Wilton maisiewilton@btinternet.com

Dear Maisie,

Sorry to have taken so long to reply, but I haven't been well again. Anyway, I'm on the up for now and ready to reply and hear the next episode!

Poor Mum! To have a double diagnosis in one day must have been utterly devastating. It's bad enough to cope with one. This is something that I know only too well. I have a close friend here who was diagnosed with breast cancer, so I am up to speed with all that it entails. Sadly for her, she is much younger than Mum, in fact she is about my age, and hoped to die quickly and peacefully, but it has not been as straightforward as that. Having made all her plans after a mastectomy, she lived and continues to live, but under the sword of Damocles. She does not find it easy, and although I do what I can to help her, it isn't much, and she suffers both physically and emotionally. In her case the shock and grief were overcome fairly rapidly - she is a toughy, rather like me - but her continued existence and pain have been a mighty trial.

It is amazing to me how thoughtless some doctors can be. Sometimes one feels no more significant than a piece of meat, something interesting to be studied and discussed with colleagues, entirely without sympathy or humanity. I hope that Mike is not made like one of those, but I can't imagine for a moment that he would be.

While I was confined to my bed, I kept thinking about how hard it must have been for you to read how difficult I found motherhood. Of course I knew that you and Tommy had not been able to have children, but you were always so gung-ho about fostering that I presumed neither of you cared too deeply. I assumed that your attitude had been that children are children, whatever their parentage, and as you both also worked with children, I thought you had plenty to fulfil your maternal and paternal instincts. Now it seems unspeakably callous of me to have written and told you how difficult I found the whole mothering bit. I'm truly sorry if I have inadvertently hurt you. How cruel life is! Why was it that the natural mothering sister was unable to have children and the unnatural mother had two?

But your children must have suffered so much in their early years, before they met you. And for Dad to call them '"our half-caste" is frankly, disgusting. I see he is still an ardent racist. Sadie sounds a real character. How have they developed? I am full of admiration for you and Tommy; to have fostered four children is amazing enough, but to have taken on children with such baggage makes it all the more incredible. Just as well there are saints like you two in this world; if the world were left to people like me it would be a darker place.

And your views on hope were interesting. I have always been driven by love. I longed for love, romantic love, sexual love, mental love. And I found it at last. But of course, everything has its price. For some people death is the greatest blessing. But hope has never been on my agenda, merely fate, which appears to have been my driving factor. It seems that we have little control of our lives and perhaps that is the reason I resigned myself to my fate.

Please don't worry about diverting from the main theme. Everything you write is fascinating to me. I am enjoying getting to know you all over again as an adult, with mature perspective. And once again I ask for your forgiveness.

I still get tired quickly, so I apologize for such a short email, but I need to have a rest.

Please continue as soon as you can. I still haven't heard the promised good ending to Ricky's tale, but I will try very hard to be patient. I know you have such a busy life and there is so much to cover first, no doubt.

With much love,

Ruth

From: Maisie Wilton maisiewilton@btinternet.com
Date: 28th February 2011
To: Ruth Braydon ruthbraydon@cedaw.com.ar

Dear Ruth,

No need to ask for forgiveness. It was just the way life turned out. And Tommy and I love our children as much as I imagine one loves one's natural children. Once we had come to terms with the fact that we were unable to have our own, we were so happy to be able to give children in need a loving home. In a way it was almost more special, because we were rescuing them from a terrible life. I suppose our experience as teachers of disabled children is why we were allowed to adopt our girls when they were old enough to understand and agree. It is incredibly difficult to adopt children in any case, and adopting children who have been abused and neglected is even more arduous. But that is as it should be. One must not be allowed to take on children without first being fully aware of what it means, but the authorities go well beyond that, often to the detriment of kind-hearted, well-intentioned couples. And most couples want to adopt a baby, so that was yet another reason for our being so glad to offer a loving home and stability to Sharon, Sadie and Joy who were all years beyond the baby stage and would have been very difficult to place with a family. And the fact that they were half Jamaican made them even less appealing to most, not to mention that they came as a parcel of three!

I'm sorry you haven't been well again. What do you keep getting? It is so unlike you to be ill; you always had such a strong constitution. Have you tried homeopathic medicine? It might prevent any more bugs. Echinacea is very helpful at building up one's immune system. I started taking it regularly ever since Mum became frail, because I didn't want to pass on any germs to her if I could help it, and it worked for me.

I'll return to Mum's story from where I left off before I write any more about Ricky, because it is really difficult to keep track of where I am if I keep jumping from one person to another. I need to write it all in chronological order, which must be very frustrating for you, Ruth, but I know I'll get in a terrible muddle if I don't, so please bear with me.

So there we were, Sharon, Alec and me, drinking tea, and waiting for Tommy to come home. Mum had been 'Grandma' to my children ever since they had come to live with us, and someone to whom they had turned whenever they felt that Tommy or I did not understand their problems or how to help them. As I have said before, Mum had an almost superhuman ability to listen, to hear what was really being said *inside* the words, and my children had often come to her to tell her their stories and to listen to her advice. She could always find something positive in any situation. She had such generous thoughts. So I suppose that's why I was rather hurt at Sharon's dismissive attitude towards the devastating news that had been delivered that morning in hospital. But with hindsight, Sharon was right. What we learnt that day was that neither Parkinson's nor breast cancer was life threatening in her case; it was to be a slow deterioration over an unknown passage of time, and one that we would all gradually become accustomed to, which we did. After all, from Sharon's perspective, we weren't under any immediate threat {and she knew everything there was to know about physical threats, poor child} but had only received information that gave us time to prepare for the progression of the diseases, nothing more. And so my children were able to give me great comfort and strength, which I had been singularly lacking in until that moment.

Tommy came home at five o'clock and took one look at me before rushing to my side and enfolding me in his warm arms. He didn't say a word; he just waited patiently until I mustered the strength to tell him between sobs what had happened. He knew I was taking Mum to hospital that morning, and as I hadn't rung him, he had assumed that no news was good news.

'My poor pet, oh my poor pet,' was all he said. He often called me 'pet', that Tyneside endearment that spoke volumes of love and tenderness when it came from his lips. 'We'll manage everything just fine, pet, don't you worry. We've already been through far more than we bargained for and survived, haven't we? This'll be no different, you'll see. Now, have you told Douglas?' As I hadn't yet, he offered at once to come with me to deliver the news, which I gratefully accepted.

We left Sharon with the younger children and asked her to begin to prepare our evening meal and drove over to Mum's to get there before Dad came home. We found her sitting in her armchair staring into space, much as she had on our return from hospital. She said she had slept a little after I had left her, but was feeling weak and shaken.

'It's the shock, Margaret,' said Tommy. 'You could do with a brandy.' And without waiting for an answer, he went into the dining room and poured her a glass. 'In fact, I think we could all do with one' he announced, as he returned with three full glasses on a tray. 'I might pour a whisky and water for Douglas in preparation, and I think I'll take him into the study and tell him there, if you both agree?' We nodded and he continued, 'When I've told him perhaps you'd come in, Maisie, and tell him exactly what the breast specialist said, because of course he is going to want to hear it all, word for word.'

The brandy brought a little colour back into Mum's cheeks and as we sat sipping our drinks I suggested that perhaps it would be a good idea if I arranged a private appointment with Mr Smythe, the Parkinson's specialist that Mr Spencer had recommended.

'Can't I just wait for a National Health appointment, Maisie? It will cost a fortune and if I have it, it won't be any the worse for waiting a few weeks.'

'No, Mum. Absolutely not. We'll pay, won't we Tommy? You can't wait weeks to find out if you have Parkinson's or not, the waiting will be hell. And anyway, *I* couldn't stand it. The sooner we know, the better. And if you do have Parkinson's, the sooner you start taking medication for it, the better you'll feel, too.'

'Maisie, you could never wait for anything, could you darling?' Mum's eyes actually twinkled and I felt a brief wave of relief. 'But I *can* wait and I don't want you two spending any more money on me. My broken hip has already cost you a fortune.'

'Margaret, please don't even consider waiting,' Tommy insisted. 'It's our pleasure and I assure you that we're not going to starve because of one specialist's bill.'

'All right then. I suppose it's better to know than live in doubt. Oh! Quick! There's Douglas's key in the lock. Go and meet him, Tommy, will you? I haven't the strength to see him till he knows.'

Tommy went into the hall and we heard them greeting each other and the note of surprise in Dad's voice, followed by the study door closing and ice clinking in a glass. Ten minutes later Tommy called to me to join them, and as I opened the door I was struck by Dad's expression of shock and horror. Mum had been right not to see him before he had assimilated the news, as he looked devastated: worse than that, he was really frightened. His normally ruddy complexion was ashen, and there were tear stains on his cheeks. Silently he held out his hand to me and pulled me towards him. I knelt beside his chair, and he put his arms around me, running his hands through my hair, something he hadn't done since I was a child.

'Oh Maisie, she's not going to die this time, is she?' he finally whispered in my ear.

'No, Dad. Definitely not. It's an appalling shock, but it's not life threatening. Mr Spencer was almost jovial about it. He said she'd certainly die of old age before either breast cancer or Parkinson's took her, so that's something, isn't it?'

'But what will become of her?' he asked. He sounded like a frightened little boy.

'I don't really know just yet. But I'll find out everything there is to know, I assure you. Mr Spencer has prescribed her drugs that will soften her breast lump and slow its growth and I hope that there will be something similar for her Parkinson's disease, if in fact she does even have it.'

'But think of Alfie Turner! What a terrible end he had! And it nearly killed his poor wife, looking after him. Whatever will become of us? I can't look after your mother the way Jean took care of Alfie. You know I can't.' And we did know, only too well, so there was no point berating him, Ruth. Certainly not then. Tommy and I had already been through a period of caring when Mum broke her hip and had discussed many times how we would manage to look after her as she aged. We knew the stakes and were quite prepared to do whatever was needed when the time came.

'Dad, Alfie had a very severe form of Parkinson's. It's unlikely that Mum has the same kind. Mr Spencer told us that there are many different types of Parkinson's, so we just have to hope that Mum has a mild one.'

'Maisie and I have planned to take Margaret to see the Parkinson's specialist as soon as possible to find out just what's in store,' Tommy said. 'The sooner we know, the faster we can make plans, and hopefully she'll not get much worse once she starts taking the correct medication.'

'That's good, Tommy. Thank you both. How is she? How did she take it?'

'Naturally, it came as a tremendous shock,' I told him. 'We were both so utterly unprepared and unsuspecting. We were hoping and naively assuming that the lump on her breast would be just a fatty mass, but to be told that it was breast cancer and that she also was in the early stage of Parkinson's was a double whammy. She's very shaken, Dad, and very worried about you and how you will take it. You must be extremely strong and *kind*. She's not up to anything much at the moment. She's just sitting in a stunned heap. But you know Mum, she'll rally eventually, but it'll take time.'

'Can she manage on her own when I go out?' he asked, his face crumpling like a man who has just been given a violent blow to his abdomen. I could read visions of forthcoming horror on his face as he imagined Mum completely unable to move, wheelchair bound, shaking from head to toe. 'I'm no good at hanging around the house all day long; I'm not used to it. And you know I'm no good at nursing and all that sort of thing.'

'Oh yes of course, Dad! Nothing has changed, at least not for the moment. It might take years before it begins to affect her, but we don't yet know what to expect, that's the trouble. That's why we want to get her to the specialist as soon as possible. So that we can prepare ourselves for the future and make any necessary plans.'

Then I told him everything that had happened that morning, but I don't think he took in half of what I said. He sipped his whisky and rubbed his eyes vigorously, as if by doing so he could wipe away the news. When there was nothing left to say, he rose to his feet and said 'I'll go and see her then,' and left the room. Tommy and I stayed where we were for a little while before we went to join them, and when we did, we found them sitting side by side on the sofa like Darby and Joan, holding each other's hands, and I have never before seen them so quiet and tender with one another. They looked up as we entered the room and smiled weak smiles. Dad nodded at me and said 'we're going to fight this together, aren't we, Margaret? I'll get the best treatment money can buy, hang the expense! What else can I do for my angel?' But that made us all dissolve into tears again, and Tommy suggested that a second drink might be a good idea.

'Are you trying to turn your mother-in-law into an old soak?' Dad laughed. And we all laughed too loudly at his pathetic attempt to lighten the leaden atmosphere.

We left them in front of *My Fair Lady* having made them poached eggs on toast.

Apparently they sat and stared, deep in their own thoughts until it was over, neither of them having heard a word, and relieved when they could go to bed and try to escape their anxiety in sleep. It took Mum about six months to come to terms with her illnesses by which time her Parkinson's was noticeably worse.

Mr Smythe was an odd man with a very unfortunate manner for a doctor. He had fiery red hair which also covered the knuckles of his huge, heavily freckled hands. His pale blue eyes were cold and practical and I thought he would be better suited slicing up specimens in a lab than dealing with the sick in a surgery. I could imagine him dissecting mice and monkeys, implanting all sorts of horrors just to see the results, without a moment's qualm about the misery he was inflicting on trapped, defenceless creatures. But he was the man to see for Parkinson's disease and we just had to put up with him, although Mum was deeply offended by his manner and after the first visit, swore she would never, under any circumstances, consult him again.

'I can confirm that you do have Parkinson's, Mrs Campbell,' he said swiftly, leaning back in his large black leather armchair and stretching his arms behind his head, as if telling her bored him. He openly glanced at the clock on the wall indicating that he was an important and busy man, and we should conclude our business with him as swiftly as possible.

'I have several questions to ask you,' I began, and he audibly sighed, Ruth. *Really!* Mum's face was a picture of incredulity and dislike, but I was not to be put off. I am not nearly so wishy-washy as I used to be. Unfortunately, this strength and determination has been learnt through necessity, dealing with the police, child protection officers and addiction advisers. I wish it had been gained otherwise.

'How do you see my mother's future, with her type of Parkinson's?'

'Oh, she'll be fine, fine,' he said, as if I were a four year old asking if my hamster had a cold.

'What do you mean, *fine?*' I pressed. 'How can she be *fine?*' The damned man sighed *again*, took another audible deep breath and said, 'I mean that it will develop quite slowly and there will not be any sudden dramatic change. Just a slow progression. Not much to worry about, in fact.'

I could have murdered him at this point. But rather than losing my temper, a delicious thought crept into my head. What would annoy him more than anything would be a whole string of such questions, and that was just what he was going to get, like it or not. So I fired one question after another until I could not think of a single thing more to ask him, while his face coloured as deep a red as his hair.

'If you don't mind, Mrs Wilton, I have other patients waiting. May I suggest that you get in touch with Parkinson's Disease Society who are very helpful in giving just the sort of information and advice that you seek. My secretary will give you one of their leaflets on your way out. I would like to see you again in three months, Mrs Campbell, to monitor your progress and alter your medication, if necessary. I'll send you an appointment card. Good morning.' And he rose from his chair and dismissed us.

'"The Caring Profession!" Mum uncharacteristically jeered as we left the hospital. 'That man is better suited to the "Decimating Profession!" Why do cruel people like him choose medicine? If you can't be kind to your patients, then you have no business treating them. He made me shake so much more, but it was with anger.'

However, Mr Smythe was right. Mum gradually began to pull herself together and slowly, very slowly, life returned to normal.

There were a few things that she could no longer do, and the list stealthily increased like a creeper growing up a stone wall, working its way into the mortar and increasing its hold. The first thing to go was her handwriting. On the initial visit to Mr Smythe, he had asked her to draw a circle, which she could only just do, and he carefully stored the piece of paper in her file. On the second visit, only three months later, she was asked to draw another circle, but this time she couldn't complete it. A year later, she could no longer even hold a pencil, do up the buttons on her blouse, peel and chop vegetables or sew. She couldn't walk very far either and sometimes I worried about her becoming agoraphobic. What happened instead was that she became lonely. She had a few visitors but had stopped going to Church because she felt everyone would look at her shaking and she felt extreme embarrassment, even though she didn't shake much. Sometimes she had fits of shaking; they were what she euphemistically called "her bad days," but she didn't shake all the time. Nevertheless, she didn't want to be an object of curiosity or sympathy.

'I can't get out much these days Maisie,' she finally admitted to me when I asked her one morning if she were bored. 'I've been active all my life but now all I seem capable of is sitting and reading or watching films. I do feel lonely as Dad likes to go and play golf most days and when he comes home he reads in his study or watches football matches. There's no doubt that I'm finding many simple jobs so much more difficult to do. It's so frustrating; it makes me want to weep.'

My eyes stung with tears hearing her speak. I was consumed with guilt. Why had I not noticed? Was I so wrapped up in my own little life that I couldn't see what was happening to my own mother? I had spent the past few years breezing in and out, preparing vegetables, taking her to the hairdressers, the library and so on, but I had obviously not really *seen* her. I had been blinded by my own busyness and I felt ashamed. I was always in a rush, and so I made a decision to spend more time with her, just sitting and talking quietly together, like we used to when I was the only one left at home. And that is what I did.

I have to finish now, Maisie. The dishwasher broke down yesterday and the electrician is here to see if he can fix it. As this firm charge by the *quarter hour*, I just want to make sure he's not spending his time gazing out of the window! Anyway, this email is already far too long, again!

With my love to you,

As ever,

Maisie

From: Ruth Braydon ruthbraydon@cedaw.com.ar
Date: 2nd March 2011
To: Maisie Wilton maisiewilton@btinternet.com

Dear Maisie,

That Mr Smythe sounds a total shit! I hope you moved immediately to someone more caring, even if he was "the man to see" if one had Parkinson's. Dear God in heaven, why is it so difficult for most specialists to have compassion? It is something I have often questioned, and my theory is that specialists are instinctively closer to science than their role as doctors, and generally take much greater interest in the *form* the disease takes, rather than the person who is afflicted. If I am right, then it would be far better for the patient if specialists were divided into two departments that worked together as a team. One department for the scientific specialists, and the other for the empathetic specialist who would deliver the news and type of treatment to be followed, in a gentle and concerned manner. Then they could huddle together in the lab *after* surgery hours and dissect and theorize to their hearts' content. And what would you speculate would be the ratio of these two types of doctors? I am prepared to bet that for every caring specialist there would be at least twenty of the scientific kind! At least my friend with breast cancer has not had to suffer such indignity. She has had the most wonderful doctors, although she has had to hold out against their advice for further radical treatment. She just doesn't want it and is refusing to have it.

But now, of course, I am dying to know if upon discovering that Mum had both Parkinson's and breast cancer, Dad reached his road to Damascus? Was this a turning point for the tough, uncaring Douglas? You said that he continued to go out all day to play golf leaving Mum feeling lonely, so I rather suspect his change of heart only lasted a day. No surprise there, then.

I agree that Mum was extremely good at listening to people, but she never seemed to be particularly good at listening to *me*. I still don't think she ever really understood me, Maisie. We were all right when we talked about other people or general topics of conversation, but in matters close to our hearts, on subjects painful to both of us, she remained closed. Perhaps this was because she knew that we would disagree and didn't want to argue with me. She was like you, an "anything for a quiet life" type. But there was a lot that we *should* have aired, and if we had, we'd both have been better for it, I'm sure. I'm not the kind to spend years in therapy, but now, at nearly sixty, I do think it has its uses. To be able to talk to someone who is completely objective, who does not know the people concerned and who is entirely on the side of his/her patient, must bring comfort to many. I've only ever wanted to forget - without the forgiving - and put it all behind me. But nevertheless I deeply regret that Mum and I never had a full and frank discussion about Dad, who was the aggravating protagonist in all our lives. Anyway, it's all too tragically late now.

Thanks again for all the long emails. Having your emails to look forward to, even with great trepidation, got me through a ghastly winter and a tough spring.

Your loving sister,

Ruth

P.S. I hope you got your dishwasher fixed without too large a bill!

From: Maisie Wilton maisiewilton@btinternet.com
Date: 7th March 2011
To: Ruth Braydon ruthbraydon@cedaw.com.ar

Dear Ruth,

Your letter made me feel so sad. I know that you and Mum had a 'love/hate' relationship and yet were quite unable to live without each other, as I recall, at least until you departed. You never failed to phone her every week and tell her your news and you were always so upbeat, that each phone call gave her a new reason to be happy. Now I realise that you probably only ever told her the good news and never mentioned how difficult your life had become with two children you didn't know what to do with, and a husband who was, more often than not, on the road. I admire your courage and strength, Ruth. You never told any of us how much you were suffering. Even though you were suffering with motherhood and boredom, suffering is suffering, whatever the cause.

But do consider Mum's impossible position, caught as she was between the devil and the deep blue sea. She loved us all, *including* Dad. You know she did. How was she to discriminate between her children and her husband? And in particular, between you and Dad? She couldn't, Ruth. No wife and mother can, at least not unless there is actual physical harm. And you couldn't expect her to do so. So she listened to us all and made her own, very private judgements, and kept them close to her heart. But she must have suffered terribly, as well. You were not the only one to suffer. We all did in our own way. Probably even Dad, who had two children he could not control and certainly never understood. It must have been tough for him, too, and I think we should allow him that at least.

On an entirely different subject, I love your concept of a two tiered specialist team! And I found myself in full agreement with your theory of the different type of specialist. I have heard that autism is often referred to as "engineers' disease" because so many engineers have autism. Engineering requires a great concentration of mind, I understand, and is therefore particularly suited to the autistic type, who is able to hyper-focus on a single subject for years at a time. I suspect that specialising in a science-based subject such as a particular field of medicine would require the same fierce concentration and dedication. I taught many autistic children in the past and Tommy has increasing numbers in his school. It is a fascinating disability and one that is at the cutting edge of science as there is still so little known about its cause and how to help those who have it. So I wouldn't be at all surprised to discover that Mr Smythe was on the autistic spectrum. He had absolutely *no* empathy, one of the most instantly noticeable traits of autism.

Sorry, but I've got to dash out. Just wanted to say how sorry I was to read your sadness.

More another day!

Lots of love,

Maisie

P.S. dishwasher fixed, at last!

From: Ruth Braydon ruthbraydon@cedaw.com.ar
Date: 8th March 2011
To: Maisie Wilton maisiewilton@btinternet.com

Dear Maisie,

Thank you for your kind words. I agree that we all suffered in our own way, but I do not accept that Dad did. I really don't think he suffered at all. If he did, it was only through sheer frustration at our not always bowing to his fierce control. I *did* expect Mum to stand up for us more than she did and I do not understand why she put up with all his bullshit.

Dad's stinginess drove me mad. I was not asking Mum to choose between her husband and her children, but just to speak openly to Dad in front of us about his ridiculous theories and refusing to pay for our further education. Why couldn't she even have had an open discussion about his behaviour to me in private? She always slid away from it and it only provoked me further. Keeping everything close to her heart was no use to us, was it?

Even though I understand him a little better now after you have told me about his tough upbringing, he still had no reason to treat us like that. He had made plenty of money and it was entirely unnecessary. Any normal man would have been thrilled that his children had gone to university, particularly someone from his background, and be happy to help them on their way to a better future than he had had. Most people who have been through that kind of deprivation usually end up *indulging* their children.

Anyway, I just wanted to put across my point of view.

Please write soon. As soon as you can.
With much love,

Ruth

From: Maisie Wilton maisiewilton@btinternet.com
Date: 10th March 2011
To: Ruth Braydon ruthbraydon@cedaw.com.ar

Dear Ruth,

Perhaps I phrased it incorrectly. What I meant to say was that I think Mum did fight our battles for us, but kept them behind closed doors. She had found it a far more effective method than having an open discussion which would have undoubtedly turned into a fierce fight and achieved nothing. You must admit whenever we did try to have that kind of discussion, it never got us anywhere. Only more and more unbearable rowing. I hated it, and I'm sure Mum hated it too. How could she not? Seeing her husband and children at each other's throats? So she took Dad off, and quietly, and in her own way, presented our case.

Of course I agree with you about Dad's stinginess. He forced me to continue to live at home the whole time I was at teacher's training college, you remember. And it was not something I enjoyed, except to be with Mum and keep her company. The best thing that ever happened to me was having my own home with Tommy. The relief of being away from Dad, and living with someone so kind and loving is inexpressible, still.

Anyway, I just wanted to clear that point. I'm going out to dinner, so I'll email again tomorrow sometime.

Much love,

Maisie

From: Ruth Braydon ruthbraydon@cedaw.com.ar
Date: 11th March 2011
To: Maisie Wilton maisiewilton@btinternet.com

Dear Maisie,

Well she didn't get very far, did she! Even behind closed doors!
That's my point!
    Please continue with the family saga . . . waiting, waiting for
more.
    Love,

    Ruth

From: Maisie Wilton maisiewilton@btinternet.com
Date: 13th March 2011
To: Ruth Braydon ruthbraydon@cedaw.com.ar

Dear Ruth,

I'm positive she was only trying her best. And that's all any of us
can do.

I will continue:

After the double diagnosis Mum became deeply depressed. As
she had never suffered from depression, we were all slow to recognise it for what it was. In fact it was Mum herself who finally
realised that she was suffering from depression. Each day I visited her she found it harder to raise a smile, and then for months
she would ask me "why can't I just die, Maisie? Every night I go
to bed and pray that I won't wake up in the morning, and each
morning I am still here. I've had a good life, but I've had enough
now and I am so frightened of the future."

There was little I could say to counter such sentiments.
Indeed, what did she have to look forward to as she opened her
eyes each morning? The drugs were affecting her memory and I
noticed that she would often ask the same question two or three
times each visit. Of course I didn't mind, and I answered each
time as if it were the first. The last thing I wanted to do was make
her feel foolish on top of her physical weakness, but she was all
too aware that her mind was far from sharp.

'I've been reading this book, Maisie,' she said one morning,
shakily holding up *Restoration*, by Rose Tremain, having to use
both hands. 'I'm almost at the end and have just realised that I

have already read it. How can that be? No one forgets a Rose Tremain! Am I losing my mind?'

'No, Mum, of course not! You've just read so many books in your life that it would take Einstein to remember each one. Anyway, what does it matter if you enjoyed a second reading? She's a stunning writer. We both reread Jane Austen frequently and enjoy her each time, so what's the difference?'

'Maisie, you were always such a bad liar,' Mum replied. And I confess I had to hide my eyes from her impenetrable gaze. 'But perhaps you're right, at my age what difference does anything make any more? But losing your mind is the most terrifying thing that could happen to anyone, don't you agree? After all, what are we without our minds? I've been thinking about this quite a lot recently and keep returning to the idea that *memory* is our mind. If we lose our memory, then who are we? Nothing but living organisms. Even animals have a memory.'

'Yes, "an elephant never forgets" and all that. But what about intelligence? Surely one's acumen would remain intact, even if one's memory becomes less reliable?'

'I'm not sure. If we lose our memory, then what use is intelligence? If one considers the most intelligent and intellectual people we can think of, it is their memory that stands out, isn't it?'

'No, I don't think so, at least not entirely. Intelligence is the ability to discriminate and discern, isn't it? Using one's intellect to interpret facts.'

'My point exactly! Because if we can't *remember* anything, then we are unable to retrieve the facts from our memory to interpret! So without a memory one is alive but unconscious, existing only through uncontrolled emotions and automatic reflexes.

Which is only slightly above the level of a vegetable, and I live in dread of becoming a vegetable, or, at the best, one of the "walking unconscious" as my Minister refers to the ignorant masses. How ghastly! What would be the point of living? That's why I'm so afraid when I forget things, Maisie.'

'But you're a long way from that, Mum. Please don't worry about it so much. It's nothing more than natural ageing. Believe me, if I thought you were showing signs of Alzheimer's I would do something about it.'

'Such as what?' Mum looked at me, her eyes twinkling at last, that anxious, far away look fading under her natural good humour.

'Oh, I don't know. Send you on a wonderful, very long holiday to The Maldives or somewhere like that, where you could enjoy every moment, every flash of flying fish and shooting star without ever having to worry about a thing. That would be truly living in the moment, and what all the world's gurus say is the right way to live, and how we *should* be living everyday.'

'So you think Alzheimer's might be a final blessing, do you Maisie?' Mum laughed.

'Now I come to think about it, it could be. So don't worry, Mum. If you don't know it's happened, you won't notice.'

'I'm not sure I like the sound of that, although I do see your point. Shall we have a cup of coffee? As I can still remember what it tastes like, I'm suddenly longing for one.'

Around that time she began to talk about euthanasia. I arrived one morning at coffee time and found her and Dad in deep discussion in an atmosphere as fraught as it had so often been when we were all living at home.

'Maisie, make yourself a cup of coffee and then come in here straight away!' Mum commanded, before I even had time to take off my jacket. 'Your father and I have been talking and I want to know what you think.' A little alarmed, I made a cup of coffee and went to join them in the sitting room. They were in "their" chairs, facing each other and at first glance looked rather like two cocks at the start of a fight.

'So tell me,' I said.

'Maisie, I want to die!' Mum said, shockingly simply and directly.

'I know, Mum. You've often told me that you wish you could just go in your sleep.'

'You *see*, Douglas! She knows!' Mum said vehemently, her triumphant blue eyes glinting, challenging Dad.

'Maisie, I want to go to that place in Switzerland where you can die, but Dad won't hear of it. That's it in a nutshell. What do you think?'

'If that's what you really want Mum, I'll back you,' I said. I didn't know what else to say, Ruth, and reading this your first reaction might be to send the social services to arrest me. But it took the heat out of the moment. I have often found with my foster children that denying their current crises, or pussyfooting around it, only leads to exacerbating their enormous sense of frustration and compounds the problem. It is far better to go straight to the centre of the cyclone, and then talk it through. Doing so takes the heat out of a situation almost immediately, and by coming straight to the point, the person with the problem at least feels that they are being taken seriously and are really listened to. So that is why I said what I did.

'I knew *you'd* understand, Maisie,' said Mum, looking at me with enormous relief, her eyes filled with the light of hope at the thought of release from her physical degeneration.

'I do *absolutely* understand, Mum,' I continued. Dad sat staring at me as if he wished he could get up and hit me, but he remained in his seat, his fingers grasping the arms of his chair, his knuckles white. I could see the beat of his pulse on the raised veins in his temples. Remember that? Always a bad sign and whenever I saw it, I used to think to myself "time to run for cover".

'I know how much you dread a slow and degrading decline. I would too. Is this the reason you want to go to Switzerland, Mum?'

'Yes, Maisie, *yes*!' said Mum with a ferocity that was surprising. 'I knew you'd understand how I feel, but Douglas is so against it. *Talk* to him *please*, darling.'

'Why are you so against it, Dad?' I asked, in as soothing and unexcitable tone as I could, because they were both extremely agitated.

'It's completely mad, the whole idea! She can't simply go and die, just like that! It's against the law and I'll be put in prison, or you will even more likely than me, for taking her there, and allowing it. Anyway, it's just not *right*, Maisie! It's illegal *and* unnatural. I hate to even think about such a dreadful thing, let alone talk about it.'

Dad was a Molotov cocktail of fear and anger about to explode, so I took a deep breath and said 'Mum, if you really want to go to Switzerland, I will take you. But first I will have to find out if it's actually possible and how to do it.'

'*See*, Douglas! *Maisie* understands!' Mum repeated, looking in triumph at Dad.

'But it may be more complicated than we think. Why don't I go online and look into it and come back tomorrow and tell you everything I've found out? How does that sound? And Dad, I promise to find out the legal situation for us both. Neither of us wants to end up in prison, do we? And Mum, of course would not want that either, would you Mum?'

'Oh God, *no!*' said Mum, and the light began to gently dawn on the possible severity of the consequences of her wishes. It was an awful situation. Dad was stricken at the thought of the sudden loss of his wife, and although the future didn't look good, I could see that he was equally terrified at the swiftly approaching prospect of having to live on his own and fend for himself.

Once the taboo subject was out in the open, Mum began to talk about her fears of taking her own life, but only after Dad had left the room, of course, because he hated religious talk.

'I'm worried that if I do it I will not be forgiven,' she said. She looked up at me, her blue eyes hesitant, shadowed with tremulous vulnerability, like those of a child needing comfort and reassurance from a parent. Grasping her meaning, I asked, 'do you mean that you fear God will not forgive you?'

'Yes, I suppose I do.'

'I can't believe that, Mum. God knows our innermost thoughts and if that's what you really need to do, He'll understand, I'm sure. And it's only Catholics who believe that suicide is a sin, and as you're not Catholic, why this sudden fear?'

'I don't believe that the Church of England condones it, either.'

'Desperate need leads to desperate measures. Blow the church and their manmade rules and hypocrisy! You have lived an exemplary life Mummy, and have given so much to so many. You

126

have the right to consider your own life and needs and not worry about ancient laws laid down by men, not God. I understand how much you fear becoming increasingly incapacitated, and how you dread the idea of ending up unable to do anything for yourself. It is extremely undignified, but do remember the Parkinson's specialist said this was very unlikely to happen. He was such a brutally direct man that I feel sure that if this was your prognosis, he would have told us when I asked him all those questions.'

'You're right, darling. Thank you. And thank you for listening to me. I've often thought of taking all those pills I have, but the fear of not dying and lying in a coma for years on end fills me with such horror that I am not brave enough to do it.'

'That's *not* a good idea, Mum. Anyway, I'm pretty sure you don't have enough to do the job properly. Doctors aren't allowed to leave more than a few days' worth of pills, specifically to prevent suicide. Taking an overdose of pills is *definitely* a worse option than dying naturally.'

As soon as I returned home I went online and looked up Dignitas, the group who offer assisted dying in Switzerland. There were pages and pages of information but nothing I read gave me the slightest hope that Mum would be a suitable candidate at that time. The euthanasia that Dignitas offers is for those who have a terminal illness and are suffering extreme pain, or have acute difficulty breathing and so on. The people they help have no hope of a cure and have already tried every available alternative. Most of the candidates have only a few weeks left to live and Mum was far too well to be considered and was not suffering much physical pain. Certainly she shook, and the lump on her breast was painful sometimes, but she was far from being at death's door. I wondered how she would take this loss of hope. I made several phone calls to check my findings with friends who work in the National Health or alternative therapies, and even phoned Dignitas in Switzerland to have my conclusions confirmed. Satisfied that I had done everything I could, I prepared myself to tell her my results the following day.

'I'm really sorry, Mum,' I began. Even this brief opening changed her look from one of hope to despair, and I watched as her body slumped into an even smaller bundle of fragile bones drowned in her now oversized clothes. 'It seems that you are not nearly ill enough to be considered. Apparently Dignitas only offers euthanasia to the terminally ill and those in chronic pain, neither of which applies to you. But if you ever reach that stage - God forbid that you do – I'll take you there, I promise you.'

There was a moment's silence as she tried to rally and put on a brave face, but I could see the effort was Herculean. She had never complained about any illness all her life, always brushing aside a bout of flu or a migraine, hating being fussed over and taking herself to bed to heal in the dark, like a wounded animal retreating to its lair. 'Sleep is the best cure,' she always said, and she has been proved right. Most doctors these days tell us that plenty of sleep and drinking lots of water are the most effective cures for ordinary illnesses. It was only when she had broken her hip in agony for a whole month that she finally admitted that she could no longer bear the pain.

'So how shall we manage in the meantime' I asked. 'What could be done to make your life enjoyable? I've been thinking of the possibility of your having a carer come in the morning, to help you get dressed and keep you company. Would you like that?'

'No, Maisie! *Certainly not*. I couldn't *bear* having anyone in the house, it would drive me crazy. I'd only worry about them all the time. How could you even think of such a thing?'

I was pretty certain that this would be her reaction, but decided to moot it as an alternative to far more desperate measures, so I plodded on. 'You *have* been rather lonely lately, Mum. You've admitted as much yourself. And I can't come around as much as I would like. I just thought that some nice lady to help you do up your buttons and perhaps water the plants and prepare lunch might be a good idea. We could look for someone who is very quiet and fond of reading, like the wonderful Mrs Norwood who looked after Emily in her last year, do you remember? Emily adored her and said she became her best friend.'

'You'll never find another Mrs Norwood, Maisie. They don't exist any more.'

'But there's no harm in trying, is there?' I suggested gently. 'What do you say? I could at least try to find someone nice and if you don't like her, I'll simply tell her that it's not working out and ask her to leave. It seems worth the experiment.'

'I'll think about it, but don't push me. I don't want to talk about it any more, I'm tired now.' So I left her, and the following morning began to search for the perfect carer/companion.

As this seems like a natural break, I will end here for today. I'm sorry it is all taking so long, but by now I hope you will understand why.

With much love,

Maisie

From: Maisie Wilton maisiewilton@btinternet.com
Date: 14th March 2011
To: Ruth Braydon ruthbraydon@cedaw.com.ar

Dear Ruth,

I was up half the night after I had written the latest email to you, as it brought back so many recent memories. Eventually I gave up any attempt to sleep, and at about 5am I went downstairs to make a cup of tea. It made me wonder if I had done the right thing, in promising to take her to Switzerland if she ever became really ill, because I had no idea how I would have achieved it. At that stage I was only all talk and bluff. But having agonised over it till breakfast time, I decided that as it had given her enormous comfort just to think that there was a get out if it came to it, I decided no harm had been done. And in the end she died in her own bed, which is what we all would choose if we could.

It only took a few days for her to agree to employ a carer. She had talked about it to Dad, who of course, was very keen. A carer would remove much of the pressure from him, particularly his guilt, which was beginning to increase each time he left the house. Nevertheless, he carried on with his everyday life regardless; but when she gave me permission to look, I could read the enormous relief in his eyes. One can't force others into roles that are unnatural or even alien to them, Ruth, as you know, even if circumstances become dire. It was also a much better alternative than euthanasia and he took to her decision with enthusiasm, and although he never offered to pay, at least he didn't mention the cost. His initial fleeting tenderness of helping "his angel in every way possible and hang the cost" lasted only one day. But

130

Tommy and I decided that we would cash some of our savings and pay for the carer ourselves if the money from Dorothea ran out. I looked up government help on the internet and found that Dad - and this will make you laugh - could apply for a carers allowance! I asked for the forms to be sent to me, and a few weeks later a health visitor came and after assessing their situation, agreed to the application. They didn't get much, and Dad magnanimously said that he would put all of it towards the carer's pay, which was big of him! I am being mean, I know, but the very thought of Dad being Mum's carer at least brought a smile to Tommy and me.

I had expected finding a carer would be a fairly easy exercise, and set about registering with the few local care agencies. But after spending a long and entirely fruitless morning on the phone, I gave up with a heavy heart and went to make myself some lunch. Mum had at last agreed, and a carer would be good for everyone, but finding the right person who was willing to do just a morning, administer pills and help with personal care and *above all be quiet,* appeared to be a surprisingly tall order. The carer had also to be willing to drive her to the hairdresser, the library and so on, and many of them did not own a car. I had naively thought that all carers performed these duties, but I was swiftly enlightened. Many refused to drive, others were too active and couldn't stand sitting quietly, and most of them were only willing to work full days, as it was difficult for them to find another client who only wanted them in the afternoon. I left my telephone number with a few agencies, having been extremely specific about the type of person that would be acceptable to Mum *and* Dad.

After a few days one of the agencies I had approached rang me, and as delicately as possible, asked me if "Mum" - which I hated straight away, why couldn't she call her Mrs Campbell, for goodness' sake – 'would mind a foreigner?'

'What do you mean by "a foreigner"? '

'Well, dear, I mean someone from Africa, or India.'

I also resented being addressed as "dear." I was *not* her "dear". I had never met the woman and my mother was not some gaga idiot to be talked about as if she were a child but like the intelligent, well-educated lady she was, with courtesy and respect. I didn't know how to address that problem, but was certain just what Dad's reaction would be at having a "foreigner" in the house. As an archetypal racist I knew he would blow a gasket, and that would ruin the whole delicate business. But how could I put it diplomatically? The agent was obviously having the same problem, because she couldn't ask me directly if I were against another race, or her agency would be closed more swiftly than an English summer. So we both skirted around the problem, ducking and weaving our way through awkward questions, until at last it was understood that an English carer would suit "Mum" best.

After several of these phone calls, I became adept at handling this problem, but of course it diminished the list of suitable carers to the bare minimum. I feared we might never find someone, and I was hoping we might at least find a nice Polish or Romanian woman, or anyone from an Eastern European country who was kind and quiet, and *white*. Mum and I agreed that it would be best if I held the first interview and if I liked the carer, I would then take her to visit Mum to see what Mum thought. After several fruitless weeks, one of the agencies telephoned.

'Is that Mrs Wilton?'

'Speaking.'

'Oh good. It's Dora here, dear, from *Dawn to Dawn 24 Hour Home Care Agency*. I have some very good news. One of my superior ladies has just finished her last placement rather earlier than expected, and I think she would suit Mum very well. She would have been my first choice, but she was already placed until this morning. Would you like to see her, dear?'

Ugh! Those "Mum" and "Dear" terms really grated. I told myself to rise above it, that this might be wonderful, until I replayed her sentence in my mind and touched the black spot.

'Why did she leave earlier than expected? What happened?'

'It's rather sad, dear, but unfortunately not unusual. The family of the lady that Inge was caring for decided that her care cost too much and that they would replace Inge with help from social services, meals on wheels and that sort of thing. They felt that their mother didn't need the level of care she was receiving. Poor old lady, she is almost bedridden and she loved Inge, and Inge loved her, but that's some families for you. Always counting the pennies.'

'That's absolutely appalling! How could anyone do such a thing? Surely she isn't capable of looking after herself most of the day if she's bedridden?'

'No, she isn't, but that's some people for you. And there's nothing any of us can do about it, either.'

'Can't you alert the social services and ask them to reassess her level of need?'

'It's not my place to interfere in other people's affairs, dear. Once my carers are no longer employed there is nothing I can do.' A silence fell as I absorbed this information. Why it should come as a shock to me, I don't know. Tommy and I had spent our lives working with special needs children as well as being long-term foster parents. I think I must have suddenly seen it from our mother's perspective and what horrors could be inflicted on her if she hadn't us to rely on and care for her, and I was shaken.

'Are you still there, dear?'

'Sorry! Yes, yes, I am,' I spluttered, as I dragged my mind back to the present.

'So would you like to see Inge? I rang you before anyone else as you sound like such a nice person. She's not English, as you can tell by her name, but she's not from a Commonwealth country either!'

I hardly gave her nationality a thought as I made an appointment for the following morning, eager to meet this supposedly wonderful carer, only fleetingly presuming that with the Christian name of Inge, she was probably Scandinavian. But never in my wildest dreams had I envisaged someone quite like Inge Walter.

And on that tantalising note I will email the latest missive!

With love as ever,

Maisie

To: Maisie Wilton maisiewilton@btinternet.com
Date: 16th March 2011
From: Ruth Braydon ruthbraydon@cedaw.com.ar

Dear Maisie,

What an intriguing end to your email! There is so much to comment upon that I hardly know where to begin. I wait with impatience to find out more about this Inge Walter. Well done for finding a carer for Mum. Thank you, Maisie. She had never previously suffered from depression, as you said. I can't imagine her lonely, either. Where did all her friends disappear to? It is very hard to live without the comfort and support of friends, particularly if one is dealing with a terminal illness. People who become terminally ill belong to a clan of fellow sufferers and it seems that only those who are experiencing it themselves can really understand what goes on in the mind of the patient. That is why it is so incredible that specialists are so often heartless. One would think that in their daily contact with the terminally ill, they would learn some compassion.

You wrote of euthanasia. You are wrong to assume that I do not agree with it. Who wants to live on in a body that is disintegrating and a mind that is failing? There are many worse alternatives to death. Why people want to cling on to life in that condition is a mystery to me. Once pain and illness take over, it is time to leave as gracefully as possible and one should not be forced into an unwilling 'existence' if one chooses not to be kept alive, although I expect Dad will be a fighter when his time comes. How right you were to support Mum when she asked to be taken to Switzerland. It is crucial to give those with terminal cancer who wish for euthanasia the comfort of knowing that if life becomes intolerable, there is a way out. But I knew before I read your discovery that she would not be a suitable candidate.

Life is such an odd thing. Rich, and so complex that I think most of us walk through it deaf and blindfolded for our time on earth, our brains asleep and only our animal instincts alert enough to prevent us from starvation. Often realisations come far too late to correct the past or to change old habits and one is left with an overwhelming sense of grief and shame at the dusk of this all too brief life. Lost opportunities and mistaken paths, lies, deceit and anger are high-lit in the eerie hours of the dead of night, under the ruthless spotlight of regret that brings every glaring fault into full, undeniable display. Here am I complaining like a child that our mother never understood me. At least I understood my own children, I made sure I didn't repeat my experience, and I talked openly to them and played with them all the time when they were young. That's what I don't understand, because they were well adjusted, normal kids when I left. And Billy was still there, the real home bird.

I spent my childhood, and my marriage - indeed my whole life until I came to Argentina - feeling like an outsider, but I've never once felt out of place here. So perhaps I'm not as odd as I had always assumed, just someone who was born in the wrong place. If people can be born in the wrong body, why can't they also be born to the wrong parents, or in the wrong country, or even in the wrong age? The only time I have felt awkward here is with the whole Latin 'adoration of children' thing. Anyway, I think society, generally, has become far too child-centric. At least in our family we were always made aware that we were second class citizens! And that was not always a bad thing. These days parents run around their children twenty-four hours a day and have no time left to nourish their marriages. Look at China, with their millions of Little Emperors. Little Tartars is what they really are. Incredibly spoilt, demanding and fat, but those precious sons will pay in spades when they reach maturity. First, there will be very few brides for them, owing to female infanticide. So unless there is a huge swing to homosexuality, they are going to have major problems in the sex department, or will have to migrate to Thailand. And second, there will be only one child to look after two ageing parents and four even older grandparents – and all on one meagre salary. Huh! So much for trying to control the population, it never works. One just has to look at the animal kingdom to see the folly of artificial manipulation. Introducing grey squirrels to the UK for example, or rabbits and cane toads to Australia. The list is endless. And the ultimate of all human monsters, Herr Hitler, who tried to produce a pure Aryan race. Human folly and arrogance is extraordinary. It is mind boggling in its blind determination to be self serving and thus, destructive. We never learn. Imagine how glorious life on earth could be for everyone if we were able to pass on knowledge from generation to generation. But it has proved impossible. Every generation starts from scratch. I've never understood why, have you? What is the point in having such a large brain if we are only able to access 10% of it? The same applies to dolphins. They have enormous brains, but charming as they are, all they have ever learnt is to perform a few simple tricks and squeak. At least human beings invented the wheel. And the pill!

You have yet to tell me how Mum died. I do hope it was not as she feared? That would be an unbearable end for me to read, and one I do not intend for myself. My poor friend with breast cancer longs to die too, but she lives on, and on. The fear of death passes surprisingly quickly for some when the end is in sight. If one is very ill, it becomes a longed-for relief, as you say it was for Mum. Even without faith in life after death. Argentina is a predominantly Catholic country, so euthanasia is deeply frowned upon, as is suicide. There is no accommodation for it and suffering is seen by the devout as "good for the soul," which I find infuriating. How can intolerable pain be good for the soul? And if one believes in life after death, why the stigma for ending it, when living is nothing but hell and misery? I sometimes ask these questions to a select few, but have yet to receive an acceptable answer.

I know nothing about autism, but felt a slight tingling of recognition in my blood as I read about the trait of lacking in empathy. It made me wonder if my missing maternity gene put me on the autistic spectrum. What do you think? Isn't there another form of autism, Asperger/Asburger something or other? How is it different to ordinary autism, and do you think I might be like that? Even if I am, it's too late to do anything about it now, except that it may help explain my behaviour to Jane and Ricky. And even Billy, if he cared to know, which I doubt.

Anyway, I'm sure that that is quite enough of my proselytising! I've done too much already. I'll email this reply and wait in anticipation for yours. So please don't delay in writing the next episode.

With very much love,

Ruth

From: Maisie Wilton maisiewilton@btinternet.com
Date: 20th March 2011
To: Ruth Braydon ruthbraydon@cedaw.com.ar

Dear Ruth,

Life is full of surprises! I had always imagined that you would
have fought to the end, too. My telling of Mum's passing is taking
so long that I will put you out of any unnecessary anxiety immediately, and tell you that she never developed dementia beyond
forgetfulness, nor reached the stage of serious physical disinteg-
ration before she died. She was in a pretty bad way the last six
months or so, but never as bad as she dreaded she might become.

And no, I do not think you are autistic, nor do you have
Asperger's Syndrome, which is the high-achieving end of the autistic spectrum. I think it is possible that we all have a slight trace
of autism. You were merely un-maternal, that's all. No sin in that,
surely? Particularly as your children were seemingly unaware of
your struggle, as we all were. So don't beat yourself up unnecessarily, Ruth. There is a wonderful Arabic proverb by Agathon
written in the 5th century B.C. which says "even God cannot
change the past." So "let go, and let God," as the saying goes! We
must, to survive.

I can't think why we have such large brains if we can't use
them, either. I have always supposed that geniuses such as Moz-
art, Einstein, Shakespeare and Wagner, who just happen to be the
four that first spring to mind, must have used a part of their brain
that is impossible for the rest of mankind to reach. As if they
were born with a brain that had not fully closed during develop-
ment, leaving an open chink through which their genius could

flow. I sometimes wonder what it must be like to be brilliant. Quite lonely I should think. The rest of mankind presenting itself as unspeakably stupid and boorish, leaving the genius with very few with whom he could communicate with any real pleasure and interest. And do you think that with great gifts comes great pain in equal measure? Are the feelings and sensitivities of the genius as highly tuned as their intellect? If that is so, I'm not too sure that I could bear the pain of the world in such intensity. Nor even the joy. Maybe there is some bliss to be had in ignorance after all.

And now I'll tell you about Inge Walter.

'Good morning, Mrs Wilton. I am Inge Walter, your worst nightmare!' she laughingly announced as I opened my front door. I looked down at a smallish middle-aged woman with an ample figure whose neat, soft grey curls were turning white at the temples. She had black oriental eyes set in a pale oval face, but apart from those two features she looked entirely European to me. Slightly knocked off my stride by such an odd opening remark, particularly when she was coming to be interviewed, I invited her into the sitting room and disappeared into the kitchen to make her a cup of coffee while I regained my composure.

White steam rose from the hot coffee and clouded Inge's glasses, and as she wiped them dry, I asked her what she meant by her odd remark. And here comes the first surprise.

'I am half Japanese and half German!' she laughed, 'your two worst enemies! And as you can hear, my accent is just like the Nazis' in those war films you British still love to watch, even after all these years. I know you wanted an English person, but here I am anyway! Did they not tell you about me at the agency? No?' she asked as I shook my head in bewilderment. What on earth would Dad make of this, I wondered, and involuntarily shuddered at the thought.

'No, they didn't. Only that you had excellent references which is by far the most important thing, of course.' And although I meant it, Inge's background presented not so much a stumbling block, as a mountain. I even wondered if our dear bigoted father would not have preferred an African, and *that's* saying something.

'So shall I stay then?' Inge laughingly inquired, and I did my best to laugh with her but as I was thinking about our father's reaction what came out instead was a nervous titter.

I took a sip of my coffee and asked her what her interests were outside caring for the elderly, and here comes the second surprise. To add to this already extraordinary background, and even though she had been brought up in Germany, she felt that her spiritual home was Israel! She had, in her middle-age, discovered Kabbalah, and was immersed in its practice and teachings. She attended Kabbalah weekends and seminars and most of her Israeli friends were Kabbahlists, if that is the correct term? I know nothing about Kabbalah except it is some sort of Jewish mysticism and very popular with the Hollywood set. But I did check up on it with Danny Levi, a very dear Jewish friend whom I met at university. I don't think you ever met him, did you? Of course I never brought him home, so maybe that's why, although come to think it, you weren't living at home then anyway. Danny is a lawyer and his father is a Rabbi, but he has a philosophers' soul and a heart as big as a harvest moon. He said Kabbalah can be divided into three types.

'Hmm. How to explain?' he said. 'Let me think . . . O.K. Kabbalah is the study of the mystical aspect of what is known as God, in order to try and find out in *human terms* what this whole God thing might mean. If I were to give you, say, a literary, or a religious analogy, it would run along these lines - in *extremely simplistic* terms, you understand? So, the first, very popular Madonna type, for want of a better example, is in literary terms the equivalent of *Heat* Magazine, and is, frankly, complete crap. The second is more serious, and is the Trollope and King James Bible Kabbalah. But the third is the *real thing* and is *never* taught to non-Jews and *particularly not* pop stars! This is the Shakespeare of Kabbalah and the Old Testament in the original Hebrew. Only Rabbis or Talmudists with the most *enormous* learning are even *allowed* to touch this subject which, in itself, is indefinable. Does that help? And now I want to know, why the question? Please don't tell me you've fallen for this nonsense also? I thought you were a free thinking Unitarian!' He laughed his huge, open, bear of a laugh and I reassured him that I was only trying to assess if a potential carer for my mother was mystical, in which case that would be fine, or mad, which would not.

'As for mystical, well, maybe she *thinks* she is and I guess that's harmless enough. It depends on how strong a convert she is and if she's going to try to convert your poor mother.'

'She didn't strike me as evangelical. Happy, even eager to talk about it, but I don't think she'd pursue the subject if there were no interest.'

'Then I think you're safe, Maisie.' And I thought so too.

The third surprise was that Inge had recently become a devotee of something called aural wiping. I don't know if you have ever come across this type of healing, Ruth, but it works by wiping clean the patient's aura and freeing up the energy flow, which reinvigorates the body and enables it to heal. I've read about it somewhere, although I can't for the life of me remember where now, of course, but was so interested in what Inge had to tell me that her interview ran from coffee until lunch time. Her references were excellent and she assured me she could sit for hours reading quietly if that was what Mum wanted. I decided she was the perfect carer, but told her it was my mother's decision and that I would tell my mother all about her, and if she were willing, bring Inge to meet her as soon as possible. Feeling full of optimism, and having long since dismissed any difficulty that might arise from Inge's parentage, I went to have coffee with Mum the following day, eager to tell her all I had discovered about Inge, and the fascinating morning I had spent with her. But before I had time to tell her anything much, our beloved mother was instantly negative and disapproving.

'But a *Japanese-German*, Maisie!' she interrupted, her face full of apprehension and disappointingly not at all excited about the prospect of my having found an quiet, intelligent woman with excellent references, who had already offered her a free trial of aural wiping.

'But she wasn't even *born* during the war, Mum! She can't be much older than me! And at least she's *half* European and from *Western* Europe too.'

I'm afraid I spoke rather sharply, and I am ashamed to say I even felt a bit hurt that she had not shown any appreciation for my weeks of effort and phone calls to find a nice companion, and had only focused on the single negative. After all, the poor woman couldn't help being born half Japanese and half German; it was just very bad luck.

'I couldn't possibly have either a Japanese or a German in the house, Maisie. And to expect me to have someone who is both is quite out of the question. Your father wouldn't tolerate it for a second; you know only too well how he feels about both races.'

'But she's so *nice*, Mum!' I expostulated. 'And well educated - *and* she's a reader. Just what you wanted. And the fault lies with Dad, have you ever considered that? You haven't a xenophobic bone in your body.'

To my amazement Mum turned up her nose as if she could smell something bad and said, 'It's not only your father, Maisie. I went through the war too, and I'm not sure that I'd like such a person looking after me. It wouldn't feel *right* somehow. I think I would feel extremely *awkward*.' I was very surprised because she was a naturally open-minded woman, but illness changes everything. I might as well tell you now that having spent her entire life thinking only of others, during the last two years of her life she became increasingly self-involved. I don't know if this was the result of her not being able to get out and about and living in constant frustration at no longer being the capable woman she had been all her life, or just plain old age. But she *changed*, Ruth. Little things, like not being able to wait for anything, happened with increasing regularity. For example, she would ask me to water the plants and when I was half way through, she would ask me to change a light bulb. I told her that I would as soon as I had finished the watering, but she couldn't wait and insisted that I did it straight away, in case I forgot. Occasionally it tested my patience, but having written it down, I now realise it was probably in case *she* forgot, which was quite likely. It seemed at the time as if she were slipping back into childish behaviours, and she even had Dad running up and down stairs and getting up from his armchair a dozen times during the evening to fetch this or do that, things that had to be done *now*. So whenever I felt irritated, I would ask myself just how well I would cope if I were in her shoes, and the answer was always the same: very badly. Then my admiration for her courage and strength of spirit would rise again, and consequently nothing seemed to be too much trouble. Nothing ever is, if there's enough love and understanding. That sounds cloyingly sentimental I know, but nevertheless it is still true.

'Won't you at least *see* her?' I was almost begging at this stage.

'I don't think so, Maisie. You know how Dad feels about the war. He's still firmly of the opinion that the only good German is a dead German, and having a German in the house, no matter how nice you say she is, would be expecting far too much of him. And as for a *Japanese*, well, just imagine what he would say! They were terribly cruel during the war and one can't be expected to get over that kind of thing. Can't you find another Mrs Norwood, as you said you would?'

I did my best to be patient and kind, and explained that most carers these days were either black or Asian and that a Japanese-German, born long after the war was over, might be the most ethnically close to an English Mrs Norwood we could hope to find.

'But can't *Jane* find me someone English?' whined Mum, sounding like a petulant child. Jane had been working at the Freeman for a few years but had often complained to me of the same problem. Many of the overseas nurses she supervised could barely take a temperature, let alone do all the tasks she had been trained to do. Even the doctors were less knowledgeable and less capable than qualified English nurses, which caused shivers to run down my back when I thought of the time Tommy was in hospital.

'Carers these days are the same sort of people you find in hospitals, Mum. You remarked the last time you went that nearly all the staff are foreigners. But we should consider ourselves lucky they want to come here to work, otherwise our hospitals would be empty.'

'What does she look like?'

'What you'd expect someone who has a German father and a Japanese mother to look like. Western, but with a Japanese face and eyes. I expect her hair used to be black, but it's short and grey now and she is shortish and plump and very nicely dressed. Will you at least give her an interview? I promise you if you don't like her, you don't need to employ her. I will continue to look, but just give her half an hour.'

'If you insist. All right. Why doesn't she come tomorrow? Douglas will be playing golf in the morning and it would probably better if he isn't here.'

'Good. I'll give her a ring and ask her to come about eleven o'clock.' And I'll think about how to deal with Dad later, I mused.

Inge arrived swathed in lose floating pale lilac, and looked rather like a large Mediterranean jelly fish. I'm sure you remember that lilac is a colour that Mum has always particularly disliked, and as I opened the door the next morning, my heart sank. Such a small thing could put Mum off her completely.

'Good morning, dear!' said Inge, walking towards Mum with her arm outstretched to shake her hand. Oh no, I thought. First the lilac clothes, and now the dear. It's a lost cause. I could have kicked myself for not having warned Inge that Mum hated to be called dear. How could I have forgotten something so fundamental? Mum responded with stiff formality that spoke volumes to me, but Inge was not to be so easily put off.

'I hear you have been feeling rather housebound and lonely

lately, and could do with a little quiet companionship. Is this right? And that you would like someone to help you dress in the morning and take you out.' I had told Inge that Mum was a deeply private person, but it obviously hadn't made much of an impression. I also became aware just how strong a German accent Inge had. Another faux pas. Mum threw me a frozen look, as if to ask what on earth I had done, telling a stranger such intimate details. And a *Japanese-German* stranger to boot.

I offered to make a cup of coffee, which Inge seemed pleased to accept, but Mum threw me another look which said just what she thought of my leaving her alone with the offending person. I took rather longer over making coffee than I had intended, as I noticed that the washing machine and dryer were both full and had finished their cycles. By the time I had sorted out the laundry and returned with three cups of coffee and a plate of biscuits, the atmosphere in the sitting room was considerably lighter.

'I have been explaining to Margaret how I learned about aural wiping,' said Inge with a delighted smile, 'and she said she would like to try it. I'm so pleased, as it's helped many of my dear friends in the past.'

'Maisie, you might like a treatment too?' asked Mum, offering it to me as a peace pipe.

'I'd be very keen to try it, Inge,' I said with almost too much enthusiasm, as it seemed we were going somewhere with this. 'I have very stiff shoulders and occasionally I have headaches as a result. Do you think it might help?'

'Certainly, certainly,' said Inge, her facing lighting up.

I looked at Inge through my mother's eyes and saw a nice, capable, middle-aged woman who was neat and clean and whose eyes shone with enthusiasm, which was infinitely preferable to mawkish compassion, which Mum would have hated. If she had been English, she would have been perfect, but would Mum, and Dad more to the point, be able to stomach her German accent and Japanese eyes? And the answer, when it came a few days later, was yes, and no, and led to a terrible row that still makes me feel sick whenever I think about it, which I studiously try to avoid.

But more of that when I have gathered my strength. So for the moment, goodbye dear Ruth!

With love as ever,

Maisie

From: Ruth Braydon ruthbraydon@cedaw.com.ar
Date: 22nd March 2011
To: Maisie Wilton maisiewilton@btinternet.com

Goodness, Maisie!

Again, I can hardly wait for the next email! This Inge Walter of
yours sounds quite a character! Did she stay, and what did Dad
make of her, that is, *if* she stayed? I can't imagine for a moment
that if Mum were not too keen to begin with, that she could have
been accepted by Dad!

I have never heard of aural wiping. Did it work for you? Perhaps you never tried it again? I don't know anything about Kabbalah either, except, as your friend Danny Levi termed it, the
Madonna variety. But I loved his explanation; it made the whole
subject clear. I never met him, as you surmised - I must have left
home when you met, but he sounds a lovely man. It is such a
tragedy when one considers all these wonderful people that Dad
never met, nor Mum, because of his insanely irrational stigmat-
isation of anyone different. He made his life extremely limited
by cutting out all the richness that variety brings. Like trying to
make a Christmas cake without adding the fruit.

I was interested to read that you do not think I am autistic.
Although it removes what could have been a convenient excuse
for my personality. Perhaps I was born in the wrong body and
should have been a man. Rod, instead of Ruth! And would that
have made me more acceptable to everyone? Men get away with
murder on the empathy front, so why can't women? Just because
a woman is not all soft and gooey like a marshmallow, she should
not be condemned as a Tartar. But it is the case. Men are terrified

149

of strong women; it makes them run a mile, as I know only too well. Unless one is Joan of Arc or Maggie Thatcher. And when I come to think of it, what about Indira Gandhi, or Golda Meir? Here we have the legendary Eva Peron, but it seems to me she was more of an arch manipulator than a leader, and she certainly knew how to play the crowd - all those Dior dresses and that large, red lip-sticked smile. I have sometimes wondered what went on between her and Peron in the bedroom. Who was on top then?!

As for Mum changing with pain, it is only to be expected. Living with chronic pain is immensely difficult, so it cannot but change even a saintly personality. Although trying to imagine Mum becoming querulous and impatient is almost as impossible as imagining Dad agreeing to a half-Japanese, half-German carer! But your patience is as deep as the ocean, Maisie. How you coped I cannot think. I must reiterate: it was as well it was you looking after Mum and not me. I would have failed miserably, I know, and so I would only have added to her distress. You are so forgiving, Maisie! And yes, sentimental too. But in your case it has only been toward the good.

And you had a row, you said? You *hate* rowing! You always have, and would abase yourself beyond reason to avoid one happening, as I recall. Although you did mention ages ago that you eventually stood up for yourself. It used to drive me mad, neither you nor Mum standing up for yourselves. So please try to write down what happened, even if it is painful. I will probably derive some sort of perverse pleasure from it, knowing me, although I do not wish you to relive it if you find it unbearable. However, I am enthralled.

I have so many questions. I will try to be patient, but please don't be too long in replying! Not much news here as I haven't been doing much. In fact I haven't been feeling terribly well recently, so I will email this short reply immediately as I am longing for your reply.

Your {impatient} sister,

Ruth

To: Ruth Braydon ruthbraydon@cedaw.com.ar
Date: 26th March 2011
From: Maisie Wilton maisiewilton@btinternet.com

Dear Ruth,

I'm sorry to hear you haven't been feeling well again, did you try the Echinacea? Whatever is the matter? Have you seen a good doctor? You just keep saying you haven't been well, but not *what with*. It is so unlike you, Ruth. Anyway, I hope you are fully recovered by the time you receive this letter.

Tonight, as I am sitting at my computer, I can hear the loud whistle of rockets whizzing towards the stars before they explode. There must be a wedding taking place nearby, but as the large coloured showers of light are reflected in the mirror to the right of my desk, my mind is cast back to one of our more eventful family bonfire nights when we were children, which I wonder if you remember. As I recall, what happened was as follows:

As usual, Dad had invited the Bracknell family, and while he went to bring us all drinks, Bert let off the first firework too close to the box, and a spark caused the whole lot to ignite. Do you remember the brief but magnificent display we had that year? The fireworks were far too close to the house and the rockets went off in every direction except upwards. Katherine wheels spun *across* the lawn and Dad rushed around frantically, trying to make sure that a rogue firework had not embedded itself into the wooden fence, or flown in through an open window setting the house on fire! We were all shrieking with laughter and delight, which made him furious, but we couldn't help it, could we? Even Mum was weeping with laughter, and the more we laughed, the more bad-tempered Dad became. We were completely out of control, just like the fireworks. I did feel sorry for Bert, though, and his darling wife Maureen, who were consumed with guilt at ruining our party. But it wasn't ruined as far as we were concerned, was it? It provided a wonderful excuse to go wild, tearing around the garden trying to stamp out the dying fireworks with our wellington boots.

I used to love bonfire night. Do you remember the steaming plates of baked potatoes filled with creamy butter, and the mountains of crispy sausages we were allowed to eat in our fingers, that one night only? And Mum's delicious, enormous apple and blackberry crumble, served with her special homemade custard which she cooked with a vanilla pod? It was also the one night of the year when we could drink as much lemonade as we liked. No wonder we were all hyper! I have continued the tradition with my children and luckily, for me, Tommy enjoys it too.

But I am putting off telling you about the row. O.K., Ruth, here goes. This won't be nearly as difficult as Ricky's story, so I might as well tell you straight away, although you will have seen by the date that it has taken me a few days to pluck up the courage to do so.

Gradually, over the course of the morning, Mum fell under Inge's spell, and after Inge left and we had discussed her attributes, Mum decided that she would try her as a carer. I was delighted, and extremely relieved, but now had to the face the problem of explaining Inge to our beloved father. Mum was adamant this should be done by me. She was too weak for such an almighty confrontation, she declared, and I agreed with her. She had struggled for nearly a year coming to terms with having both breast cancer and Parkinson's disease, and was increasingly handicapped by the latter, and I wanted to protect her as much as I could from any unnecessary upset. But Inge's background could not be hidden. Her eyes and face were Japanese and her accent markedly German, even though she had lived in the UK for over thirty years. I discussed the problem with Tommy that evening who suggested we invite Dad for a drink and tell him on our own territory. It seemed the obvious answer, and Dad accepted the invitation and came for his whisky and water the following evening.

'So what have I been summoned to discuss?' he asked, as he took his drink from Tommy while looking at me.

'Good news, on the whole,' I began. 'I've found a very nice carer for Mum, and Mum has met her and likes her very much. She comes with wonderful references from several families she worked for, looking after their elderly parents.'

'Well done, Maisie.' Dad smiled up at me from the depths of an armchair. 'That's grand. It'll take a load off my mind knowing that I can go out without worrying about her and leaving her alone. What hours will she do and how much does she charge?' Ever the businessman.

'Mum thought it would suit her best if she came about 8.30 in the morning to help her get dressed, and stay till 11.30. She's quite willing to prepare the lunch and set the table so all Mum will have to do is turn on the oven. She's about £15 an hour and although Tommy and I will pay for as long as we can, your carer's allowance will help quite a bit.'

'Right. Of course you can have that, I said so before. It means I can go and play golf in the morning, then. Your mother and I are early risers, and as she has a nap in the afternoon it'll free me up for most of the day.'

Good old Dad. He never changes. He's the living example of that wonderful Tyneside saying, "Self first, self last, and if there's owt left over, self again."

'And you'll pay did you say? I expect you can afford it as you're still working, Tommy. I didn't realise that teaching paid so well.'

'It doesn't, compared to business, Douglas. But I've been the headmaster of St Bede's for some time now, and a head receives quite a good salary.'

'That's a relief, because I've been retired for so long that my savings have shrunk to almost nothing, although the property market remains strong. Thank God I still have all those houses to let. The income is very handy and if things get really tight, I can always sell one or two. So what's she called, this carer?'

Here goes I thought, and I took a deep breath and said 'Inge Walter.'

'What? What did you say, Maisie?'

'I said she's called "Inge Walter".' My voice was irritatingly unsteady. The explosion was instant. Dad's face was a picture of anger and disgust. The smile of relief which had been sitting there so pleasantly a moment ago, suddenly gone, like a black cloud moving across the sun, blotting out all the light.

'You're not serious? Don't tell me you've gone and employed a bloody German, Maisie.'

There was nothing for it but to come out with the whole truth. I glanced at Tommy who gave me a smile of encouragement and a sly wink as I threw myself into the lion's den.

'Not quite, Dad.'

'What do you mean, "not quite"? How can you be "not quite" German? Either you are or you're not. Which is it? Unless she's a Yid. You're *not* going to tell me she's a Yid, are you?'

'No, Dad, she's definitely not Jewish.'

'Well that's something, I suppose. So what *is* she then? Get on with it, girl!'

'Her father was German, but an ordinary German, not a Nazi, and her mother was Japanese. They have been dead for years, Dad, and Inge was born long after the war.' But before I could finish he shot out of his chair and, pushing his enraged face into mine began yelling 'I am *never, ever,* going to agree to have a Kraut or a Nip in my house, is that clear? And certainly not someone who's both! You must be out of your bloody mind, Maisie!'

As he screamed at me, Inge's opening remark "I am your worst nightmare", flashed through my mind before my own nightmare began. Now we come to the bit I hate. I am ashamed of myself. I have replayed this ghastly evening in my mind so often, and I wish at this point I could shout "Cut!" like a film director, and stop there. But I didn't; instead I lost my temper and shouted back. I never shout. I hate shouting and rows. I hate anyone losing their temper, especially me.

'If you'd think of someone else apart from yourself for once, you selfish, self-centred old bigot, you wouldn't say such terrible things!'

'How dare you!' he yelled back, his face turning an ugly puce. 'You stupid, naive little woman. You've never been in a war; you have absolutely no idea what you're talking about. The Nips were the cruellest of the lot and there's no such thing as a "good" German. Ask any of your precious Yid friends and they'll tell you. You're just an idiot, lefty, interfering do-gooder. A pain in the neck socialist and the reason this country has gone to the dogs.'

'Well, why don't you try to do some good yourself for once?

It's always Tommy and me. We do all the caring, pay all the bills and all we hear is you whinging about money and your stupid golf!'

'You'd have a lot more money if you hadn't taken those black bastards into your home! It's your own fault. It's like the bloody United Nations in here, and they smell, too.'

That did it, I'm afraid Ruth. Whatever control I still had was lost at this point. Dad had never accepted my children and it caused me a lifetime of grief. If it hadn't been for Mum being so loving and wonderful to them, we would have moved years ago. I cannot abide racism in any form, and it may not surprise you to know that my children never went to visit Mum when Dad was there, and he never came over to our house unless he was invited, and he was only ever invited when they were out. It had been this way ever since we adopted the girls, and I had lived with this miserable state of affairs, a sort of unspoken truce, ever since. And he had never met Mike's lovely African/Asian - now Australian wife, and their two children. It was his loss, but nevertheless it was a very unpleasant situation to have lived with for so much of my life, and a very difficult one to explain to my children as they grew up.

'You are the most revolting man I have *ever* met!' I shouted back. 'You're nothing but an ignorant bigot and you've succeeded in tearing our family apart. *No wonder* Mike hates you so much and Ruth is living in Argentina! I wish I could leave too, but I love my mother and think of her welfare.'

I had never spoken to Dad like that before. Ever. I am fifty-five years old and finally, I told him what I thought of him. But I wish I hadn't. It only made things worse. Rows always make things worse and we say things in anger in the heat of the moment that should never have been said, and are almost always better left unsaid. I know the current thinking is to say it like it is, for want of a better expression, but I am old fashioned and find the British stiff upper lip by far the better solution. No good ever came of telling the brutal truth and the damage left in its wake is irreparable - the scars remain forever. Mostly they never even heal to scar tissue, but remain an open sore that continues till death to refester at each reliving. Dad has always had a chip on his shoulder about his lack of education, as you know all too well, and I think it was my calling him 'ignorant' that pushed him over the edge.

'I've stood by your mother all my life!' Dad screamed back at me. 'Don't you dare try to accuse me of not looking after her. Your brother made his own bed long ago and that was his choice, and Ruth is as stubborn as a mule, marrying that longhaired, guitar playing, git! You've no idea what I've had to put up with with those two, so don't you start laying into me. Nobody forced you to foster those black brats and nothing will ever make me like them.'

The two of us were inches from each other like drunken Saturday night yobs, squaring up for a fight.

'Now, now, you two. Calm *down* will you?' interjected Tommy, anxiously leaning forward towards us and waiving his hands in a calming gesture that I dismissed.

'*No*, Tommy! I *will* have my say. I *will* speak the truth to him at last, however much he hates to hear it! Don't try to stop me! I'm going to tell you, Dad, what I've felt about you *my entire life*. That you are the most *horrible, cruel* man I have *ever met!* You made my childhood *a misery* with your bullying, and I only stayed at home to protect my mother from you and because I was terrified of you. But guess what? I'm not terrified *any longer.* I just *hate* you, just like Ruth and Mike. It's not my fault you're my father, just as it isn't my adopted children's fault their father is black. I'd rather have had *anyone* than you as my father. *Of course* you stood by Mum! Why wouldn't you? She's been your slave all your married life, doing your books, charming your workers. They *loved* her. They only worked for you because of her, whatever stupid ideas you might have about your being the best employer in the area. It was *Mum* who made you, in *every way.* But now she can't be your slave any more, so you will have *any carer that she chooses.* So shut your *bigoted mouth* for once in your life. As long as my mother . . .'

Dad's hand snapped across my face with the force of a Sten gun and Tommy, who had watched me lose it in utter astonishment, stepped in, nifty as a boxer, and pulled Dad away from me before he could hit me again, but they both lost their balance and Dad crashed to the floor, just as I heard the front door opening. A second later Sadie walked into the room. She took one look at the scene in front of her, slammed the door and tore upstairs and locked herself in her bedroom. I had forgotten she was coming over for dinner. She was at university then, reading anthropology and living with her boyfriend, but she came home every Wednesday evening when he went to rugby training - only that particular week it had been changed to Thursday. She only ever wanted to eat roast chicken with home made chips and salad and we would catch up on each other's news and listen to any fears and woes she might have to tell us of her life, her friends and her studies.

Tommy rushed to help Dad to his feet, but Dad shoved him away growling, *'Don't touch me!'* before returning to me.

'Whatever's got into you?' he snarled, staring at my rapidly reddening cheek. 'You're talking like a mad woman.'

'Sit down, for goodness sake Douglas' Tommy insisted. 'And calm down both of you. I'll get you another whisky.' My eyes pricked with tears and my cheek smarted, but I was still shaking with impotent rage. It was as if a lifetime of loathing and fear had been unleashed and I was terrified that I would do something dreadful. I had an overwhelming urge to rush at him and smash him to bits with my bare hands. It was a terrible feeling. I felt completely out of control, like a wild animal. I had to get out, away from him before I killed him.

'I meant *every word* I said!' I shouted at him as I burst from the room and grabbed my jacket from the bottom of the stairs. Shoving my keys in my jeans pocket, I ran out of the house and into the street, tears pouring down my face. I hadn't cried like that since Dad used to tease me every Saturday morning for "turning into a Yid." I had thought I had thought through and come to terms with my childhood family problems decades ago, but I was shaken to the core by the power and depth of my emotions, and walked without noticing where I was going for over an hour, until I found myself in the large Catholic cemetery on the edge of the city. It was still open, and I lowered the solid handle on the heavy black Victorian wrought-iron gates and let myself in, closing them behind me as if I were shutting out the world. I found a damp bench in the centre of the cemetery and sat down. I must have been there for a long time, as it was black dark when I became aware that I was frozen and shaking with cold and misery. I made myself even more unhappy by replaying the scene over and over again in my mind, and then worrying about Sadie, and that I hadn't cooked the chicken. Eventually I got up and began to walk home. I had left in such a rush that I hadn't taken my mobile with me and to add to my misery, I worried about Tommy worrying about me. How had he managed with Dad? Had he made dinner? Was everything all right at home? What on earth were we going to do about Inge? How had Dad and Tommy parted? What did Dad say to Mum when he got home, and on and on, until I found myself outside a corner shop and impulsively went in and bought a packet of cigarettes and a lighter. I hadn't smoked for more than thirty years, but at that moment it seemed the only thing I could do to relieve me from my guilt and distress. Of course I felt as sick as a child smoking his first fag, but I forced myself to smoke it right down to the filter anyway, and then took a taxi home.

'Maisie, thank God you're back!' Tommy engulfed me in his arms and kissed the top of my head. 'Are you OK? That was quite a showdown! I didn't know you had it in you, pet. It certainly shook the old man. Come and have something to eat. Sadie and I are in the kitchen, and the chicken's still warm.'

He put his arm around my waist and guided me like a child into the kitchen. Sadie jumped to her feet and hugged and kissed me, then pulling away, looked anxiously into my eyes.

'Maisie, are you all right? Tommy and I've been so worried about you! You just ran out of the house without saying goodbye, or where you were going. You've *never* done anything like that before. What on earth has happened to you?'

'I'm fine now, Sadie. I just let off rather of lot of steam and told my father just what I thought of him. I'm fine, darling, don't worry. Now let's have a nice glass of wine, that is, if we've got any. Have we Tommy? And tell me how you managed Douglas after I left, please.'

'There's a bottle of red wine under the stairs I think,' Tommy said, rising to his feet. 'Would you like a glass of that?' I nodded.

'And Dad?' I asked.

'Well, he calmed down eventually after you left, but it took over an hour. He was still furious, but deeply shaken by your sudden explosion. Actually, I must say I was surprised too. Now what caused that, Maisie? Anyway, we can talk about it another time,' he said, as I threw him a look which told him it was not something I wished to discuss in front of Sadie.

'When it comes down to it, Douglas is an old man and he was very upset at having hit you, and so hard too. I was amazed at his strength, but of course he hit you with his golf swing. You're going to have a real shiner there tomorrow. While I'm thinking of it, I'll get the arnica cream and you'd better take the pills too, or some people will think it was me having a go at you!'

He opened the cupboard beside the hob and took down the tube of arnica cream and a small bottle of arnica pills, and placed them in front of me.

'He was very, very distressed that you said you hated him. He claims he had absolutely no idea of your feelings, and although he's never been here while the children are around, I was astonished at the depth of his denial that this was not normal family behaviour. He can't even mention Mike's name, or Ruth's! I think he suddenly became aware you're all he has left, and he realised it'll be you and me who'll look after him if Margaret dies first, and he foresaw a very lonely old age ahead of him without us, and it frightened him. He left humbled and full of contrition; it was rather touching to see, actually, and he asked me to ask you to forgive him. His last words were "if this Inge woman is what Margaret wants, she can have her, but I'll still never be in the house at the same time."

'Well, that's something. A small achievement after a terrible row. I'm also very shaken at having lost it so badly with him, Tommy. I just had to run away before I did something even worse that I would regret for the rest of my life. And I regret what I said tonight, or I should say, I deeply regret the way it all came out. Now I feel ashamed and guilty, and don't know what to do.'

Sadie reached across the table and took my cold hand in her warm brown one. Her huge round hazel eyes locked mine which were red rimmed.

'Maisie, you are the most patient and loving person in *the whole world*. I couldn't have stood a father like yours *for a second*. He doesn't deserve you for his daughter. Don't even give it a thought. We all know who you are. You're a *saint,* isn't she Tommy? Where would the three of us be without you two? You saved our lives, Maisie, never forget that. He's just a horrible old man and I'm really sorry for you that he's your father. At least I don't have to look after mine. He can rot in hell!'

I was so tired, exhausted by now, and I felt tears trickle down my face.

'Thank you, darling. You're my angel, too. Tommy and I would have been lonely old people, too, without you girls and Alec to make a family. Now let's change the subject. Tell me your news. You always cheer me up.' And she did. Sadie has a wit as sharp as a razor, and is a delightful mimic. In ten minutes she had us in stitches with tales of her tutors' philandering and by the time she left we were all feeling much brighter. She gave me an especially long hug at the front door, then skipped out into the road to catch the bus back to her flat, happy as Larry again.

After we had cleared the dishes Tommy insisted on running me a hot bath.

'I've put lavender oil in it, Maisie. From the bottle that Jane gave you for Christmas. She said it's very relaxing.'

By the time we got to bed, I was crying again and Tommy held me and rocked me, stroking my hair and murmuring endearments until the worst of it had subsided.

'What's the matter, pet? What triggered your explosion?'

'I don't know Tommy - that's the truth. Apart from the obvious answer of over fifty years of repression, I thought of nothing else as I froze on the park bench in the cemetery. I wonder if I'm just worn out with caring, or parenting, or both. We haven't had a real break for nearly twenty years. Bringing up the girls has been hard work, although it was a great joy too, of course, but they had so much baggage. Then there have been years and years of hell and anxiety over Ricky, and now Mum is so frail and needs me. Perhaps I'm feeling my age, but Tommy, can I tell you something else I am very ashamed about? I've begun to fantasize about getting on a plane to *anywhere* just to escape for a while. Completely alone. Are you shocked? Do you think that's terrible? Do you ever feel like that? Please say you do, otherwise I think I'm going out of my mind.'

'Everyone feels like that from time to time, and you certainly don't have to explain yourself to me. And yes, I have thoughts along those lines too, sometimes. It's perfectly normal, my pet. I see totally exhausted parents at school all the time. Everyone with a disabled child feels like that - you've seen it yourself. But it's the guilt of even *having* those feelings which seems to be the worst. Think of all those tragic, exhausted, mothers of disabled children who *have* been driven to suicide, and have taken their children with them. I think you're suffering from carer's fatigue and that's what this is all about. I should have noticed it long before you got so close to the edge. I'm so sorry Maisie, I feel really ashamed that I didn't. Perhaps when you've got Inge settled in you should go away for a week. I'm trapped at the moment because the new term's only just started, but why don't you go and have a really relaxing break at a spa hotel, or something like that? God knows you deserve it.'

'What I don't know is what I've done to deserve you, Tommy. You're the most wonderful understanding man in the whole world. No wonder there are so many parents desperate to get their children into your school.'

'Not even a bit of it. I'm just an ordinary man who struggles to find answers just like everyone else.'

And then he held me in his arms and I fell into a deep sleep and slept like the dead till morning.

So now you know. Warts and all.

With very much love,

Maisie

From: Ruth Braydon <u>ruthbraydon@cedaw.com.ar</u>
Date: 28th March 2011
To: Maisie Wilton <u>maisiewilton@btinternet.com</u>

My Dear Maisie,

When I read your letter I jumped to my feet and shouted *hoorah!* At long last! Congratulations! I was filled with amazement that you *finally did it* - you told the mean old bigot just what you thought of him, even if it took you half a lifetime to get there! *Well done* little sister, really, *very* well done. But I could kill the old man for hitting you; you must have rattled him extremely badly. You say "warts and all", but to me you will always come up smelling of roses, for it seems impossible for you to do anything unkind. And there is no need to feel ashamed of the memory, you must have been hiding a boiling volcano underneath your gentle exterior, and that is *not* good for one's health. Far better out than in, has always been my motto. And there comes a time in one's life when bullying should no longer be tolerated. Of course, it should *never* be tolerated in the first place. What does continue to surprise me is that you would *never* have put up with anyone else being bullied, and yet you suffered it all your life when it was directed at you. Why did you allow it, Maisie? And after the row, did Dad stop bullying you, or did life continue as before, once the heat had died down? Did the leopard even *begin* to change his spots?

What equally surprised me was that you even *contemplated* taking a half-Japanese, half-German into their house. I understand you had little choice and thought it was preferable to a black or an Asian carer, but not by much Maisie! At least she wasn't Jewish! It reminded me of those terrible years after you had read *The Diary of Anne Frank,* which had a profound affect on you. And because of it, you read many other books about the holocaust despite Dad's constant gibing at your "turning yourself into a Yid" and demanding "were you going to go to Synagogue next?" Do you remember how he used to tease you every Saturday morning, asking if you were off to Synagogue and if you had learnt Hebrew yet? No wonder you never brought Danny Levi home. I dreaded Saturday mornings because of his going on at you like that. That was why I found that job at the day nursery for you. Not for you to add to your savings towards buying the puppy you longed for all your life but never got, but just to get you out of the house on Saturdays. I realised that once the football match was on in the afternoon he seemed to forget about it until the following week, but it was years before he tired of his "joke" as he called it, and whenever you cried, he told you not to be so stupid, he was only teasing. You were so young, and Mike and I did everything we could think of to keep you out of Dad's way on Saturdays, but we weren't always successful. Talk about a German joke being no laughing matter! Dad could out-do any German with his heavy-handed humour any time.

I was very interested to read about your feelings of wanting to run away. Dare I say, I even felt a little vindicated. Were you unaware what you had written, and had been simply caught up in replaying the past? Had you forgotten to whom you were writing? The family bolter? The disgraced mother and wife? Whatever the reason, you have had a taste of those feelings and in doing so, I hope it will make my bolting less heinous and a little more understandable. There is nothing like slipping on another's shoes, even if for only a moment, to engender understanding of unfamiliar territory and as a result, a measure of compassion. Not that I am asking for compassion - God knows I don't deserve it. But I would like to you to feel a little less harshly about me, that's all.

Your daughter, Sadie, appears to be a strong character. She is very much my type of woman; no unnecessary airy-fairy graces, just the truth, straight up. And so passionate, too. Now she is grown up, I imagine her as a coffee coloured Boadicea, brave, proud and strong, fighting for what she knows to be right and not to be put off. You have been lucky with your children, Maisie. But in truth, I doubt luck had anything to do with it, having Tommy and you as their foster parents. I could barely manage normal motherhood, let alone taking on four children who were not my own, and even less, spending my working life looking after disabled ones. You two are a wonderful couple. Billy and I might have made a perfect couple if we had been able to swap roles. Then he could have stayed at home with the kids and I would have travelled all over the world instead. Pity I never learned to play the guitar!

I laughed out loud when I read about the bonfire party! *Of course* I remember it!

It was one of the few genuinely joyful moments of our youth. Especially as even Mum joined in the crazy hilarity and would not be put down by Dad for once. He was like some sort of fear-driven fireman, wasn't he? But what you don't know, dear little sister, was that it was *Freddie's* sparkler that started the great explosion, and it was not Bert's fault at all! You see Freddie and I, who were both about nine at the time I think, were having a contest to see who could hold onto their sparkler, without gloves, for the longest time before letting go. We were both rather nervous of sparklers and Freddie, who had lit his first, watched with rising terror as the brilliant orangey–red core crept towards the bottom of the metal spike, and when he didn't dare hold it a second longer, he dropped it straight into the box of fireworks. I seem to remember telling him that it didn't matter, that the sparkler had probably gone out before it fell into the box, but of course, only moments later, we realised my mistake! And to this day I don't think either Freddie or I have ever owned up to the truth! Poor Bert took such a verbal beating from Dad, but Freddie and I reckoned that Bert could deal with it far better than we could. Can you image what Dad would have done if he had known the truth? I wonder what happened to Freddie? Do you have any idea? I missed him so much when the whole family moved to Surrey. He was my best 'mate' as we called each other. I could play all the boy games with him and he never minded my bossing him about. It took me almost a year to get over his departure and because we were so young, we never bothered to keep in touch. Ah well, such is life. We are mere solitary stars moving across a vast universe, and only rarely do we make meaningful contact with one another.

I really enjoy reading about our childhood, at least the funny parts, which are all too few. But now I am dying to know what happened after the row. Did Dad back down?

Hard, if not almost impossible to imagine. But Maisie, you haven't told me a single other thing about Ricky since 8th March! I am trying to be patient, but please hurry up and get round to it. Now I am now the wearer of *the waiting shoes*. Karma.

With much love,

Ruth

From: Maisie Wilton maisiewilton@btinternet.com
Date: 1st April 2011
To: Ruth Braydon ruthbraydon@cedaw.com.ar

My Dear Ruth,

April Fool's Day! The date reminds me that next month will be 1st May, and each May Day I recall my childhood attempts at saving. I tried hard to save as much as I could after reading *The Diary of Anne Frank,* once it became clear to me that I would never be allowed a puppy. In my ten year old mind I thought that if the political situation ever became as bad in England as it had been in Europe during the Second World War, it might be up to me to save us all! It was during the Cold War and the world seemed full of very real danger to me, even though it was years before the Russians invaded Czechoslovakia and Philby was un-masked as a traitorous double agent.

Yes, Dad's teasing was really awful. But what distressed me most was that he genuinely thought it was just a bit of fun, and now I suppose that's why he would get so angry when I cried. Why would I cry when he was only joking? "Can't she see that?" he'd yell at Mum. And she wasn't able to stop him, or get him to understand that it was not funny, either. The few times she did try, he became so incensed he'd yell at her as well, until I begged him to stop. Later on I told Mum that I was very sorry for crying, it was over nothing, and that she was never to stand up for me again because I was quite capable of standing up for myself. Huh! If only I had been, but I just couldn't. You know, you were right when you used to call me a "little drip" - I was. But thank you for getting me out of the house on Saturday mornings! I genuinely believed, right up until your last email, that you found me the job so I could save up for a dog! I realise even more how lucky I was to have such a strong and protective older sister.

I think Dad might very well have strung you up that bonfire night, had he known! And Freddie beside you! I don't know what happened to the Bracknell family either, except that after they had lived in Surrey for a few years, they moved to Germany, because Bert was posted there. He was in the Royal Engineers, wasn't he? Anyway, I think that after the move to Germany both families lost touch with one another, apart from sending Christmas cards. I used to adore Freddie. He was so good looking, with those mysterious deep navy blue eyes and jet black hair that fell over them. My five year old heart was consumed with jealousy of your friendship, and you would *never* let me play with you! I wonder if Freddie was the first person I ever fell in love with. He certainly cast a powerful spell over me, as I have only ever been attracted to dark haired, blue eyed men since, rather like your gypsy. Even thinking about him now brings a lump to my throat! And there you were, having all the fun and intimacy with him, without the faintest clue of the storm raging in my feverish heart! When did you first fall in love? Were you also extremely young?

I know you are waiting to hear about Ricky, but as I am in full flow about Mum's carer, I'll continue with that, if you don't mind. As I said, I *will* tell you everything, but you can see now what a lot there is to tell. Ten years is a very long time.

To return to the leopard, who yes, did improve for a while. But Ruth, I didn't change until just before Mum died. It infuriates me, but even at over fifty, he could still put the fear of God in me. I just seemed to wither in his presence. Of course I hated myself for it, but his bullying was so ingrained in me, that I'd always rather back down than fight. That's why I was so shaken to have fought back - do you understand now? It was the first time I had *ever* stood up to him, but it cost me. I felt sick for days afterwards. You know how I hated rowing and losing control of myself and that's why I put up with it, to answer your earlier question. It always seemed a preferable alternative to a screaming match. Over fifty years of training is a difficult habit to break. But the row *did* have a beneficial effect, and it happened like this:

I went to Mum's the next morning full of dread, wondering and afraid to ask what had happened when Dad had come home last night. My left cheek was swollen and a large bruise had worked its way to the surface during the night, but with the help of arnica and cover-up, I managed to disguise it the best I could. Mum's eyes weren't good and with something on her mind, she didn't notice my swollen cheek, and to my amazement she greeted me with a bright, cheerful smile. The first I'd seen in months.

'Maisie! I'm so glad you've come, darling. The most amazing thing happened last night and I've been longing to tell you all about it. I knew Dad went to have a drink with you yesterday evening, but I didn't know if there was a particular reason why. Anyway, he came home quite a different man and told me, before he'd even taken off his coat, that if I wanted to have Inge, I could. That it was my decision and if I liked her, then it was fine with him. But that's not all! He even offered to pay for her! He said he'd sell some of his shares which should pay her salary for quite a while, and if I still needed someone after that money was used up, well, he'd just sell some more! I was so astonished I didn't know how to reply, so I just said, "Thank you, Douglas. I do like her and think I would enjoy her company." Well, what do you think of that?'

'That's wonderful news, Mum' I replied, trying to appear pleased rather than completely gob smacked, which was more accurate. It was almost as if Dad had been on his own road to Damascus so great was his volte face. I wondered how long it would last, thinking of the leopard and his spots. 'I'm so glad. Although I doubt Dad will be around when she's here, but that's why she's coming, isn't it, to look after you when you're alone, and to keep you company?'

'Let's ring the agency *now*, Maisie, and tell them. Would you do it? I might as well start her straight away, before she's taken by someone else.'

I went to the phone and called Dora at *Dawn to Dawn 24 Hour Home Care Agency.*

'I *knew* you'd like her, and Mum too. I'm so glad, dear. I'll ring Inge straight away because I know she's waiting to hear from me. We'll invoice you on a weekly basis, if that's all right? And Inge will bring a book with her and fill in what she has done every day, so that we're all clear.'

'What sort of things does she need to write?' I asked, curious.

'Only how Mum is and what medication she's administered to her, and that sort of thing. We have to do it by law, you know.'

'Oh, I see. That's probably a good idea.'

'Yes, it is. It's to protect Mum more than anything. There've been some nasty cases that no doubt you'll have read about in the papers, and now every carer has to keep a daily record.'

Inge started the following morning, and Dad was already on the golf course by the time she arrived. It was a blustery autumn day and the leaves had already begun to fall and were swirling around the air in tight circles before collecting in tidy piles in the corners of buildings. Long pointed clouds that looked like swordfish, stretched across the sky. We had had the driest September in decades and the parched earth was dust-bowl dry. The trees had already lost most of their leaves, and according to the newspapers this early onset of autumn was due to drought. It was early October and I was still watering my plant pots in the garden, and I looked up at the sky with farmers' eyes and prayed for rain before I got into my car and drove over to Mum's to help her settle in with Inge, and deal with any teething problems.

'Good morning, Maisie!' Inge greeted me at the front door. She had opened it before I had time to insert my key. 'Your mother and I are doing very well and she is downstairs and dressed, drinking a coffee. Would you like one also?'

I felt a little odd being treated like a guest in our mother's house, but accepted the coffee, and made the most of the few minutes alone with Mum, while Inge was busy making it for me in the kitchen.

'Everything going OK?' I asked a little tentatively.

'She's absolutely marvellous, Maisie, Mum said, much to my relief. 'She has a light touch and is discreet while helping me dress. She's already given me one of her treatments and I feel better already! Would you like one too?'

'I'd love one, Mum, but not today. I have to go to a meeting with the social services about Joy's progress, and what will happen when she is ready for college when she's 18, so I'd rather save it up for a more relaxed time.'

'You've done a miraculous job with those girls. I've been

telling Inge all about them and what you and Tommy have done. She's very interested and would love to talk to you about them.'

I was slightly taken aback. After all, Inge had only been with Mum for three hours and I felt raped by her knowing so much about my family so quickly. I know that the word 'rape' is too strong, yet I can't think of a softer one at the moment, although it did occur to me that this must have been exactly how Mum felt when Inge first came, so I swallowed my pride and drank my coffee. Perhaps "invaded and unwillingly exposed" is a better use of words to describe my feelings.

Months passed, Christmas and New Year came and went and Inge became entrenched, as necessary to the family as mortar is to bricks. She became a part of the structure of our daily lives and we all grew to trust and love her. This must have been a great relief to Dad, I assumed, although I had not seen him since the row except for Christmas Day. We stood our ground and those terrible words hung in the air between us, like sharpened Samurai swords waiting to reopen so severely inflicted wounds. How I regretted what I had said, Ruth! I wish it could all be undone as no good had come from it. Dad and I were like silent enemies whose only link was our love of Mum. I know that you would not feel like this, but you and I had always been so different in our approach to life. You were born an Amazon, outspoken and fearless, and so clever with words. Quick witted and keen minded, few could defeat you in verbal warfare. I was just a quaking shadow of fear and doubt who hid behind you and Mike. And even now, although I am far braver than I ever was, I am still a coward when it comes to speaking the truth and am much more comfortable in dissembling. And what is the truth apart from the obvious list not to kill, or steal, and so on? I have asked myself this a thousand times and still I can't come up with an acceptable answer. Each one of us is only capable of viewing life from what he or she perceives it to mean, according to what each individual has understood and experienced, and this is the only truth we can ever really know. So I think there can only be personal truths, unique to every one of us, and that the concept of a collective memory is a fallacy. I don't believe in it, just as I do not believe in collective Karma. Individual memories are extremely selective in what one unconsciously chooses to remember or forget, and if something in one's past is too painful, for example, one buries it as deeply as one can in the darkest corner of one's unconscious mind. And I do not consider that to be a bad place for grievous memories, although I know whole battalions of psychiatrists would vehemently disagree with me. I would far rather try to forgive and forget, choosing to remember only what was sweet. And I suppose this is the main difference between us. Both you and Mike chose never to forgive or forget, but to put it all behind you and move on. I have been told that my way is the coward's way out, that one must face and destroy one's demons in order to be truly free. Truly free, indeed! It is impossible - no one can ever be *truly* free, it is simply not part of the human condition. The closest one will ever get to freedom and happiness comes from having an open loving heart and a deliberately poor memory of any bad in the past. Why would anyone want to relive something that was extremely painful the first time round? It strikes me as mental masochism. I am often astonished at what Tommy remembers, and *how* he remembers things from the past, and what I choose to remember, and consider important. Even in intimate families reminiscing together, a story might emerge which would cause the siblings to look at each other with incredulity, as they had all been present at the same event and yet there were three of four very different and equally compelling versions and interpretations of what had taken place. Look at the truths we have discovered in our emails where we have revealed our real thoughts and interpretations of our own past. How does one interpret those truths? Which one is the closest to the real truth, and who has the right to say which it is? In my opinion there is no one person who has the right to say which one is the right one, because they are *all* right.

As I have digressed again, I'll finish for today. And I need to take our dog to the vet this afternoon. Like all working cockers, she occasionally pulls a muscle in her foot, and I think she has done so again, as she has been limping since yesterday afternoon. Cassie is our fifth working cocker and without doubt the one we all love the best.

With very much love,

Maisie

P.S. Regarding your comment about my wanting to run away occasionally. Point taken, but the difference between you and me is that I *didn't*.

From: Ruth Braydon <u>ruthbraydon@cedaw.com.ar</u>
Date: 3rd April 2011
To: Maisie Wilton <u>maisiewilton@btinternet.com</u>

Dear Maisie,

You have said how deeply you regretted your blow-out with Dad
more than once. Maisie, life is too short for regret and he deserved it. I beg you not to give it another thought. Move on like
Mike and me! I'm sure you didn't say anything he didn't need to
hear, nor had needed to hear for most of his life. My only regret
is that I was not there to witness it.

You asked when I first fell in love. I can tell you exactly. It was
at North Hill Primary school - I was six, and he was called Peter.
There was a school dance or some sort of party and I remember
to this day the feeling of blood rushing through my ears so loudly
that I could hardly hear the music as I danced with Peter. I can't
remember his surname, only that he had the same effect on me
that Freddie had on you, and I adored him! Do you suppose we
were rather precocious? Five and six is very young to fall in love,
and extremely young to be aware of such feelings. Do you think
we knew it was love at such a tender age, or did we attach the
term much later, once we had learned to name the emotion? I
would like to have been able to ask Freud what he thought. He'd
have probably just nodded his head. After all, his entire theory
was based on the dominance of sex in human behaviour.

And another thing. Although I said in response to your feelings a while ago about hope being greater than love, that I'd
resigned my life to fate, it was a stupid, glib comment. I do not
believe in Karma/Kismet/Fate or any other type of wishy/washy

woowoo/voodoo nonsense. Life just is what it is, which is simple, really. Glorious and ghastly, triumphant and tragic and there is nothing we mortals can do to affect or control a single moment of it. We have only two choices; to grab each golden moment and hang onto it with all our strength, or give way to wallowing in our misfortune. As for fate, it is complete rubbish, as are all forms of religion, however well meant. Man-made to control people through fear. And there is *nothing* as powerful as fear, except, perhaps, acute physical pain. As you know only too well, still living in fear of our father! Catholics and all superstition be damned! It can be very trying living in a Catholic country, but I rise above it and ignore it all, while admiring those who selflessly give their lives to others, even in the name of religion.

So there!

I hope Cassie is better now.

Lots of love,

Ruth

P.S. Ouch, again!

From: Maisie Wilton maisiewilton@btinternet.com
Date: 8th April 2011
To: Ruth Braydon ruthbraydon@cedaw.com.ar

Dear Ruth,

Thanks for your support. Cassie is fine now, sitting at my feet looking longingly through the French windows at a fat jay which is gobbling up all the bread on my bird table.

I'll continue from where I left off.

At the beginning of February of the following year, I took Alec over to visit Mum. He hadn't seen her since Christmas and had just been offered a new job with one of the top accountancy firms in the country and was thrilled, and dying to tell her the good news. We arrived just after lunch and I opened the door with my key and shouted "Hello!" The house was eerily still and I wandered into the kitchen to find the oven on and a plate with dried up leftover lunch on it, including the knife and fork! I took out the plate and turned off the oven and, increasingly worried, went upstairs. No one was there, but Mum's bedroom was in disarray with a towel thrown on the floor and blood stains on the carpet. I called out again into the disturbing silence and then to Alec who was downstairs in the sitting room.

'Something's not right, Alec. No one's at home and there's blood on a towel in Grandma's bathroom. And pillows are scattered everywhere. I'll phone Dad's mobile to find out what on earth has happened.'

I had hardly spoken a word to Dad for months, but took a deep breath and dialled his mobile. He answered straight away.

'We're at the R.V.I., Maisie. Your mother had a fall and has hit her head badly. We're waiting to see a doctor.'

'Why didn't you call me, Dad?' I almost shouted in my anxiety.

'Your mother thought you were at a meeting today, so we took a taxi to the hospital.'

'For goodness' sake Dad, what meeting? Never mind though, I'm coming straight over. What happened?'

'We think she got up too quickly and fell over, and smashed her glasses into her face. She's all covered in blood and it looks awful, Maisie. There's skin hanging over one eye and she can't see.'

'Just wait there, Dad, and try not to worry. I'm on my way. OK?'

I dropped Alec off at home and drove like Schumacher to the R.V.I. There had been another local outbreak of swine flu and before I could gain access I had to fill out numerous forms and wash my hands with some foul smelling antiseptic gloop that hung in plastic bags by the entry door. Mad with frustration and anxiety, I found them at last in a ward filled with old people, some even in plaster, whose frail, stick-like limbs were hanging from winches above their beds.

'Oh Maisie!' said Mum, and I had to hang on to the end of her bed to stop myself from fainting. She had a large flap of skin hanging over her left eye and was clearly extremely agitated and uncomfortable. I controlled myself, and taking a deep breath asked what had happened, and who had been to see them since they arrived at hospital.

'Douglas' was all she could say, as she looked at him to tell me. I could see she was as white as a ghost as she turned her battered face towards me, her sunken eyes locking onto mine as, with a trembling finger, she pointed to her open wound. I smiled a sympathetic smile and went to her bedside and took hold of her thin, frail hand and rested it in mine, on top of the coarse hospital sheet.

'Well, Dad? What happened? You said she had a fall, but how did she fall?'

'I think she must have fainted, Maisie,' Dad said, looking anxiously at me and then at Mum in turn, as if by doing so he could ascertain the truth. 'I heard a loud crash not long after she'd gone upstairs to go to the loo. We were in the middle of lunch and why she didn't go downstairs, I don't know. I called out but she didn't reply, so I ran upstairs and found her lying on the bedroom floor covered in blood.'

'Why on earth didn't you call me?' I asked, my voice full of anger.

'Your mother thought that you were busy at a meeting with the social service,' he answered apologetically. 'And so I called an ambulance and we came here. We've been here about three hours I think, but we haven't seen a doctor yet, just a nurse who gave her a bed and a nighty.'

'You look exhausted Dad. Why don't you go home now and I'll stay with Mum?'

'OK. If you think so, Maisie.' And without a seconds' hesitation he left, having given Mum a quick kiss on the cheek and a pat on her hand. Dad can't stand the sight of blood. He's incredibly squeamish for a bully.

'Right. I'll go and speak to the duty nurse and see what's going on,' I told Mum. But it wasn't that simple. Mum's bladder control had been getting worse and worse and she needed to go to the loo very often. She had been in hospital for three hours without a single visit and was desperate.

'Please help me go to the loo first, Maisie' she begged.

'Of course, Mum.' But it proved to be quite a mission getting her off the high gurney and on to her very wobbly legs. The loo seemed to be miles away and we almost didn't make it. There were several stops on the way to pause for breath and energy renewal, but when we got there it was occupied. There was nowhere to sit down while she waited and I didn't think she could stand for more than a few moments at a time. I grabbed an unoccupied wheelchair that I spotted nearby and sat her in it, but she became very distressed in case "someone else might need it more that I do, Maisie."

I found myself behaving in quite an authoritative, almost stroppy, manner and told her that she needed it and I would deal with the consequences.

'That's just the sort of thing Ruth would have said,' she said, smiling up at me, and I latched onto the hope that lay in her humour, as a survivor of a shipwreck might cling to a fallen mast.

Several hours passed with many more such urgent trips to the loo, and with each visit the distance seemed to increase by at least one kilometre. She hadn't eaten her lunch or had a drink since the morning, and I could see she was becoming worryingly dehydrated and weak. I rushed off to the hospital shop to buy a cup of tea and a sandwich, but the queue was long and it took ages before I returned through the miles of labyrinthine corridors with a spilt half-cup of tea and a curling cheese sandwich, and she was in a terrible state when I returned. I had missed the doctor, who was going to take her into surgery and stitch her face, and who had told her that she must spend the night in hospital, which filled her with horror. She pleaded with me to take her home afterwards, but I was sure the doctor would not allow it. Her face needed stitches urgently before the lose skin stuck over her eye began to harden, but she had to wait until he had time to do it. He had promised it would be done sometime that evening, but as he didn't know when, it meant staying over night so she could be monitored afterwards. It was terrible, and I tried my best to soothe her.

'It seems there's nothing we can do tonight, Mum. I'm so sorry. At least they can stitch your face before it becomes worse and after all, it will only be one night. Please try to manage that, will you, and I'll be back in the morning to take you straight home. After all, if you don't let the doctor stitch you up tonight, you'll be left with an awful mess on your forehead and you wouldn't want that for the sake of just one night here, would you?'

Having been a natural beauty all her life, vanity kicked in. She agreed, so long as I promised to collect her the following morning. I rushed back to her house and packed her nighty and slippers, a wash bag and a book, and by the time I returned to the hospital she had already been in surgery and had large angry black stitches across the bridge of her nose and down the centre of her forehead.

'How does it look, Maisie? I'm going to be a terrible fright for the rest of my life, aren't I?'

'It certainly looks better than it did, Mum. And the good news is that the skin on the face heals better than anywhere else on the body, which is why facelifts work so well. You might have a bit of a lump between your eyebrows, but let's hope not. Can I help you put on your own nighty?'

'I'm too tired to bother, darling. And I'll be out tomorrow morning. Where are my things? My own clothes and shoes?'

I looked in the cupboard beside her bed and found them all thrown in together, so I rescued her trousers and folded them neatly and put her blouse on top of them and the shoes on the bottom. By the time I had settled her down for the night and returned home, it was after 11pm. I fell into bed exhausted, and got up again at 7a.m. to shower and make my way back to the hospital. I had a long wait. Apparently Mum could not be discharged until the doctor had seen her, and even then only after he had checked her blood test results and found them to be satisfactory. But first he had to complete his morning round, so we had no alternative but to sit and wait, and we waited all morning and then half the afternoon. It was ghastly. The ward was packed and I had trouble finding a spare chair to sit on. I had only just recovered from a spasm in my lower back and found sitting for a long time quite painful. My back seized up after an hour and I had to keep getting up and walking around. Mum made half-hourly trips to the loo, which, with the struggle to get her on and off the impossibly high hospital bed, was a ten-minute round trip taking the shortest route to the nearest toilet, and then struggling to help her up onto it again. She tried to read, but her concentration wasn't up to it, so I sat at her bedside and read the paper hour after hour, with our only diversion her frequent trips to the loo.

What was extraordinary was from that accident until her death, Mum lost all physical inhibitions, which was entirely contrary to her nature. Do you remember how distasteful she had always found what she euphemistically called our "lavatory humour" when we were kids, and how she hated farting and any other form of vulgarity? She and Dad had always been extremely private in those matters, and I'll never forget how shocked she was when you told her that Billy often chatted to you when he was on the loo and you were in your bedroom. She was appalled, and simply could not understand why anyone would do that, or *want* to do it in the first place, let alone accept such behaviour. In the end she decided it was because Billy was a musician, and artistic people always behave oddly and as you were probably a natural bohemian, being married to Billy had brought out that side of your nature! Well, that time in hospital she lost all sense of dignity. Each time she climbed down from her bed to go to the loo she seemed completely unaware that the hospital nighty had ridden up to her waist and was open at the back, and her bottom was fully exposed to all and sundry. And she wasn't bothered by it in the least! I did my best to support her as she walked, having pulled her nighty down and holding her dressing gown around her shoulders to cover her bare bottom, but really, Ruth, she couldn't have cared less.

It wasn't until after three in the afternoon that the doctor finally came to see her. He apologized for keeping her waiting so long, but the blood test results had taken all that time to return. The good news was they were fine, and he was able to discharge her. He explained that her fall had most likely been caused by a sudden drop in blood pressure when she had stood up too quickly, and that from now on she must stand up very slowly and support herself on the back of a chair while she counted to twenty before she walked anywhere. She had fallen face down like a stone, and her glasses had been forced into her face. The stitches had repaired the damage and they could be removed by a nurse at her local surgery. She was very relieved she would not have to come back to hospital to have them taken out.

At long last she was allowed to go home. An Indian nurse came to help her get ready, but seeing our mother flinging the blankets off her and exposing herself to the world like a photo in a sex magazine, she loudly tut-tutted her disapproval, her brows tightly knitted together as she drew the curtains around the cubicle as quickly as she could.

'Hang on a second, Mum! Just wait a moment will you?' I begged, as our dear mother tried to scramble out of bed in full view of everyone passing. This was the last straw for the woman lying in her bed opposite.

'I've seen more of that woman's fanny in the last twenty-four hours than I've seen of my own throughout my *entire life!*' she bellowed in broad Tyneside, and I flushed scarlet in embarrassment for our mother, who either didn't hear her, or didn't care.

The nurse said she would bring us a wheelchair and would push Mum to the hospital door for me because I was worried about aggravating my tender back, but she disappeared and didn't return. I helped Mum into her dressing gown and slid her swollen purple feet into her worn slippers, and she sat on the edge of the lowered bed clutching a grey plastic hospital bag on her lap which held her few belongings. She looked like an earthquake survivor. Her soft silver hair was an unbrushed tangled mess, and dried blood had stuck to it and clung in ugly streaks across her dressing gown. She was the epitome of what she dreaded she might become, and I was so glad there were no mirrors. Old age sucks, Ruth! There is absolutely nothing to recommend it, and watching our mother deteriorate only strengthened my conviction that this is so. I have no desire to live beyond my strength and usefulness in life. Just what kind of cruel cosmic trick is it to make people suffer so much at the *end* of their lives, when they have already been through their allotted share of pain and trials and are worn out, and have no strength left for more? All we human beings long for is a peaceful death in our own beds free from pain, but only the very few and extremely fortunate do so.

I gave up waiting for the wheelchair and went in search of one myself. Having found one, I pushed it into the cubicle and put the brakes on. Like all hospital wheelchairs it was heavy and un-wieldy and I thought I would aggravate my back less if I pulled it, rather than trying to push the damn thing.

'Can you manage going backwards, Mum? Will it make you feel dizzy?'

'Anything to get me home, darling.'

So, as gently as possible, I pulled her along the corridors to the far end of the hospital which was the entrance nearest to the car park, with Mum looking like a battered, exhausted refugee flee-ing a war zone and I, too closely resembling Tevye the milkman pulling his cart around Anatevka, in *Fiddler on the Roof.*

'Just stay here and *don't move* while I go and collect the car' I instructed, as I walked towards the ticket machine to pay for my parking.

'And where do you think I could go?' Mum asked, raising her eyes in humour.

I ran outside into the freezing midwinter wind and drove my car as quickly as I could to the entrance and went inside to help her out of the wheelchair, but the wheelchair was empty! Impos-sible! Where on earth could she have gone? She couldn't walk more than a few feet unaided and I ran to the nearest loo to see if she had taken herself there and called out, but there was no reply. My throat began to close up in panic as I dashed up and down the hospital corridors looking for her, but I couldn't find her anywhere. So I ran outside and scoured the bleak, grey landscape, but I couldn't imagine that she would have gone outside wearing only her dressing gown in the bitter cold and of course, she was nowhere to be seen. Not knowing what else to do, I ran towards the car park and halfway there noticed a small gathering of people surrounding someone. In the middle of the circle was our mother, looking tiny and frail, still clutching her grey plastic hospital bag, her hair blowing in the wind and staring at one of the women in dazed bewilderment. As I approached I could hear her asking Mum very slowly and clearly, as if she were talking to a child, 'Are you from the hospital, dear? Are you alone?'

'It's OK!' I called. 'She's my mother and I'm here to take her home!'

Three incredulous faces turned to stare at me, obviously thinking that I had abandoned my old mother in the freezing wind.

'Mum, why on earth didn't you stay inside?' I asked. I was thoroughly shaken up and consequently furious with her.

'I just didn't want you to have to drive all that way, Maisie,' she answered as if it were perfectly reasonable to get out of her wheelchair and walk outside in freezing temperatures wearing next to nothing. 'So I thought I'd help you by coming halfway to meet you.'

'Oh Mum! You should have just waited inside in the warmth *as we agreed!* You'll catch your death of cold out here. Come on, let's get to the car as quickly as possible.' I turned to thank the astonished group and we shuffled off with as much speed as she was able towards the car, but before we had taken more than a few steps, one of them called out, 'You ought to be ashamed of yourself leaving your poor old mother out in the cold like that! It's wicked! That's what it is, wicked!'

It seems quite amusing now, reading what I have written to you, but believe me, it certainly wasn't at the time, Ruth. Mum's fall on her face followed only a few months after my major row with Dad, and I was feeling disorientated and worn out. I never managed to take the spa break that Tommy had offered, and that winter seemed interminable, dragging on and on, with one trouble after another. It was a bad time, but we survived. No choice. We just had to get on with it. "Put up and shut up" as Dad used to quote endlessly to us. These days it seems to me that the whole world whinges all the time. Whinging about their rights and wanting everything immediately without having the money to pay for it, but expecting the government to foot the bill.

I am sounding unpleasantly like our father, so I'll stop immediately and take Cassie out for a walk. A bit of fresh air might blow away the unpleasant memories. If I can avoid the Burger King and racks of Heat magazine, and fat, smoking, teenager mothers in hideous leggings and white plastic high heels, stuffing their babies with chips on the way to the park! The good old northeast! Plus ça change.

With much love,

Maisie

From: Ruth Braydon ruthbraydon@cedaw.com.ar
Date: 9th April 2011
To: Maisie Wilton maisiewilton@btinternet.com

Dear Maisie,

You should have finished your last letter "Yours disgusted, Royal Tunbridge Wells!" However, joking aside, I whole-heartedly agree with you. At least in Buenos Aires there isn't the obesity that I have read is rapidly becoming epidemic in the U.K. People here love to go out to eat and drink, but they do so with friends and family and consequently one doesn't find gangs of drunken youths rampaging the streets. That kind of behaviour is kept for political rallies! This is a Latin country and passions fly high, of course, and the dancing is wild, but it's a controlled wildness, {even though that's a contradiction in terms}, which is far more sexually arousing than overexposed flesh. Titillation is in the tension, and my God, it is exciting! Argentines invented the tango, and I doubt there is a more erotic dance, with its origin in brothels and bars. I can't think of another dance where the male and female bodies are held quite so close. In tango one dances cheek to cheek and chest to chest, and legs are placed between one's partner's legs. Flirtatious looks are integral, and even if one's partner is not particularly attractive, the dance will make him so.

Too late for Mum now, but there has been a fairly recent study which showed that tango dancing had significant beneficial effects for those with Parkinson's disease. As Mum always loved dancing, it might have been fun for her. I've just conjured up a delicious picture of Mum learning to tango partnered with your Japanese-German Inge! And another, of a floor full of gyrating

Parkinson's patients trying to get their shaking limbs to follow the moves. It would look more like Saint Vitus's dance, than a rendition of the tango. But you will think I am being cruel. I don't mean to be, it is just my black humour which sometimes takes over. As you so rightly said, old age sucks. No medical interference for me. When my time's up, so be it.

Please write and tell me how well, I hope, Mum recovered from her fall. Your letters relate one ghastly misfortune after another. Our poor mother! How much she suffered during her last few years on earth. First her broken hip, then the double diagnosis and now a terrible fall. Why all this should happen to one who lived such an exemplary life seems unspeakably cruel. No wonder she wanted to die! I would want to die if I had only half of what she had to suffer. I did laugh at the story of her getting up from her wheelchair and walking out into the cold to save you the bother of having to drive up to the hospital door. How typical of our mother, always trying to make things easier for everyone else, at her own expense. The description of you pulling her along the hospital corridor looking like Tevye dragging his milk cart carrying Fruma-Sarah was pure black comedy. Under the circumstances, humour is the only way to deal with tragedy. My friend who has breast cancer regularly visits the Hospice of the Sisters of Santa Ángela to help out when she feels well enough. The last time she went she came to have tea with me afterwards and told me the following story.

Apparently one of the patients is a defrocked priest who has spent his life since his public shaming trying to catch up with every missed romantic opportunity during twenty years as priest to a small town outside Buenos Aires. His fall from grace came when he was asked to offer a room and board to a destitute young girl who had just arrived in the town in return for housekeeping, cooking and cleaning. As he had struggled unsuccessfully on his own since his previous housekeeper had died, he was only too pleased to do his Christian duty in return for a decent meal and a clean house and clothes.

Maria, for that was the young girl's name, {is there any other girl's name in a Catholic country?} was at first shy and dutiful and performed every task required of her. Not only was she an excellent cook, but she also looked after the chickens, washed and mended the priest's filthy cassocks and within weeks had the parsonage cleaner than it had ever been.

Our priest was of course, delighted. He grew plump on Maria's delicious cooking, slept well within his clean sheets and began to convey a previously lacking sense of gravitas to his congregation in his clean, pressed cassock and his freshly trimmed hair and beard. But with the nutritious food and a good night's sleep undisturbed by bed bugs he grew randy, and Maria's breathtaking beauty began to overwhelm him each time they met. He struggled every moment of the day chastising himself for his lustful thoughts, but his nights were torture and beyond his control. Sleep, once so sweet to him, began to desert him. Instead he was filled with dreams of Maria's plump breasts which so deliciously filled and overflowed her tightly laced blouse as she kneaded his daily bread, and he desired her to the point of madness. But he was not the only male to notice her virtues. Young men from all over the town began to call on the priest to ask for spiritual advice. As had been his custom, the priest offered each guest a cup of coffee, which Maria now prepared and presented. Once Maria had served the coffee, the priest and his guest fell into a heavy silence, as each had his thoughts entirely consumed by the voluptuous young woman and their passionate desire to hold her. All religious thoughts evaporated from the young man's mind {as well as the priest's} and they struggled to make conversation before each young man made as rapid a departure as he could.

But one late summer morning the priest came home unusually early from mass. It was harvest time and the farmers had decided to gather in the grain while the weather held. Maria, who was not expecting anyone to be around at that time of day, was washing outside just behind the rosemary hedge, and was singing gypsy love songs as she soaped her glorious body. This was too much for our priest, who, tearing off his clothes and revealing a truly magnificent virgin cock, declared his undying love and devotion for his housekeeper. To his delight, instead of screaming in terror and calling for the police, Maria enfolded him within her beautiful breasts and made all his dreams come true.

Thus began an intense relationship, until the day the priest discovered that he was not the only recipient of her affections. One night he found he could not concentrate on his evening devotions and so rather earlier than usual, he crept towards her room, slipping off his cassock in readiness, on the way. But when he reached her bedroom door, he heard to his horror her familiar sounds of ecstasy coming from the other side. Flinging open the door, he discovered her in the arms of a handsome young farmer who had been one of the more regular members of his congregation to come and seek his advice. With a cry like a wounded bull, he threw himself upon the couple and tore the young man from his embrace and throwing him to the floor, began beating him. Maria screamed for him to stop and begged his forgiveness, but it was too late, the tumult had roused the village and like a storm all the young men rushed to defend their beautiful Maria.

The priest was caught wearing nothing but his glasses and was marched into town where he was held in a cell until he was called to stand before his bishop and defrocked.

But Maria had left her mark. She was not the innocent the whole village had supposed her to be, but a professional who had been chased from her home town for giving the local males a virulent strain of the clap. The angry priest spent the rest of his life vigorously spreading the disease to every young woman he could find, until it eventually overcame him and he ended up at the hospice, where his lack of repentance was a great concern to the nuns who tended him.

But that was not the end. He was on a quest to punish all women; therefore he did not flinch at attempting to seduce the younger nuns, with, so I'm told, some success. The poor older nuns were quite at a loss to know what to do with a fallen priest, for whom they misguidedly felt they owed respect. So they placed him in a house for the terminally ill with only a few others which stood apart from the main convent and took him to mass five times a day. But even this did not break the resolve of our errant priest, who quickly found joy with the few dying women, who in turn eagerly surrendered to his physical attributes when they felt well enough and who had nothing to lose as they were already beyond hope of a cure.

So a curious thing happened at the hospice. The nuns decided to turn a blind eye to the activity in their midst considering it safer to leave our priest where he could do no harm but where he gave the women he pleasured a few last moments of joy before their end came! Isn't it a wonderful story of how to deal with adversity in life? No harm done and much fun enjoyed on the way!

I can't tell you how much I am enjoying your emails, Maisie.

Even though much of what you write is about pain and loss, you also express your thoughts so well, and you write about things that I find fascinating. It seems that at last I am getting to know my little sister in adulthood, and am discovering her to be a deeply thoughtful and wonderful person, and someone I wish I had known when I had the chance. So I am trying to make up for lost time, Maisie!

Write soon, for who knows what the future holds? Think of our defrocked priest!

With very much love,

Ruth

From: Maisie Wilton maisiewilton@btinternet.com
Date: 13th April 2011
To: Ruth Braydon ruthbraydon@cedaw.com.ar

My Dear Ruth,

Your priest story really made Tommy and me laugh! I agree with
you that black humour often saves the day when one is in the
midst of tragedy. How tolerant of the nuns at the hospice and
also how wonderful of them to think of the joy he gave those
poor dying women in their last few weeks. I think Catholics often have to employ a particularly creative interpretation of their
vows in order for their faith to withstand modern pressures. For
example, do you remember my school friend Virginia Sinclair?
She was Catholic and she married and had three children. But
her marriage turned sour and she met someone else whom she
wanted to marry – but she wanted a Catholic wedding. Virginia took her problem to her priest, who asked if her husband had
beaten her, drank or abused her or her children in any way?

'No? That's a pity' he said, 'because those are excellent reasons
for an annulment.

But tell me my dear, did you, before you married your husband *really truly* want to marry him? Or were you perhaps co-
erced by your parents against your will, when you would rather
not have married him at all, but did so out of good Christian
duty to your family?'

And with this type of questioning between the priest and Virginia, it was agreed that at only twenty-one, Virginia had *not*
freely and willingly agreed to marry her husband, and so the
Catholic Church was able to annul her marriage. And as her first

marriage had never taken place, she was allowed to marry her new love in a Catholic Church with her three, now illegitimate, children in attendance, and the sin of divorce had been avoided.

But onto the next episode of our mother's decline.

Inge took good care of Mum and gradually her wound healed, and once the stitches were removed by your dear, gentle Jane, and the redness had died down, she was able to cover the scar with makeup; but as I had suspected, she was left with a lump above the bridge of her nose. However, the fall had shaken her confidence, and although her face had healed, the accident took away much of her remaining strength and energy.

Inge began to stay all morning and cooked lunch and washed up the pots and pans before she left at one o'clock. I brought frozen homemade meals and filled her freezer so that all Inge had to do was warm up the dishes and cook the vegetables. Mum still liked to feel in control of the kitchen as she had always been a delicate cook, and she used the kitchen timer all morning to remind her to ask Inge to put the water on to boil for the potatoes, and again to take them off the gas and keep them warm in the lower oven till lunch time. This process necessitated her getting up and down most of the morning which at least kept her moving, but she would insist on boiling the potato water by half past eleven, and consequently their vegetables were overcooked mush. Only once did I comment on her 'dead food' and she replied, "But that's the way we like them Maisie, nice and soft."

Each day after lunch, Mum went upstairs to rest, but as the months passed she often didn't come downstairs again in the evening, preferring to remain in her bedroom and in her dressing gown for the rest of the day. She liked to sit in her comfortable large armchair with the footrest and watch old videos on the small television next to her bed. Gradually she began to dress less and less frequently; her clothes had become too much trouble to put on and take off even with Inge's help, and after her morning shower she was much more comfortable in one of her long dressing gowns with just a pair of pants underneath. But soon she had to stop even wearing her pants as she frequently didn't quite manage to shuffle to the loo in time and even if she did, it took her too long to lift her floor-length dressing gown and then lower her pants, so she also began to smell of urine. She didn't seem to notice, at least she never remarked upon it and it was kept under control with her daily shower which she still managed to take by herself, but was finding increasingly exhausting. I bought a packet of incontinence pants from Boots, but it took her even longer to lower them than her own thin ones, because her frail hands shook so, and each time she went to the loo she soaked another pair. So she gave up underwear altogether.

One morning Inge took me upstairs. She had been changing Mum's bed and showed me the mattress.

'I think poor Margaret is beginning to wet the bed a little at night, Maisie. Do you think we could put a rubber sheet over the mattress to protect it? I've often had to do this for my other ladies, and it makes them much more comfortable.'

'What a good idea, Inge. I'll go and buy one this morning, but don't say a word about it to Mum. She's having a hard time trying to hold on to the remaining scrap of dignity she has left, and she would be acutely embarrassed if she knew that we knew about it.'

'Of course I won't say a single word!' Inge promised, and when I went to buy a rubber sheet I discovered that since my children had needed them, they had been vastly improved, and these days were made with a soft towelling top, which would be much more comfortable and wouldn't rustle or make one sweat, as the old style had done.

Not only was she rarely getting dressed, but she was unable to go out any more, and had no desire to do so, either. I worried that as she was taking almost no exercise her muscles would deteriorate even further, and so I arranged for a physiotherapist to come and give her some simple exercises to do. We began to bring in more help which included a local hairdresser and a beautician. She needed someone to cut and file her finger nails and her toe nails, as her hands shook so much she was beyond taking care of them herself. She could no longer hold a book, but Inge suggested that she rest her book on a cushion on her lap and that worked very well, holding back the pages with a clothes peg. Inge and I tried to do all we could to make her comfortable and keep her looking nice, as she wanted, but her spirit was very low and she talked all the time of death. In an attempt to take her mind off her circumstances, I asked her if she could make me a tape of stories from her life so that I had a complete record to give to my children.

'I don't think my life has been interesting enough, Maisie. And anyway, you know most of it already.'

'But I'm sure there'll be new things that you will remember once you start, Mum, and as you know I have always loved to hear family history. Shall I buy you a small tape recorder and whenever you are in the mood, you could speak into it?'

'If you think it's a good idea.'

For the next few months, whenever she had the energy, Mum talked into the tape recorder. Sometimes a few weeks would pass when she didn't feel up to it, and there were other times when she spoke into it every day. On those days when I went to visit her, she would tell me what she had remembered and we would have a pleasant trip down memory lane which brightened her morning, or so I hoped. Anything was better than long depressing conversations about death and how eagerly she desired it.

'I was just remembering the first time I met Douglas,' she announced as I walked into her sitting room one morning. Her face held a soft, faraway look and I could see that she was right there, in the past, and it was as fresh and real to her as the present was to me. Before I had even taken off my coat, she continued. 'I'm sure you know the story about how my parents disapproved of him from the beginning, but I have never told a soul what happened before our meeting, I was always far too ashamed. Anyway, the only people who really cared about it are dead now, so I don't mind talking about it.'

'What is this? Do we have a family skeleton in our cupboard?' I laughed.

'Indeed we do,' she answered with complete equanimity. 'And the skeleton belongs entirely to me.'

'Go on' I said, intrigued. I shucked off my jacket and, flinging it over Dad's chair, sat beside her on the sofa. She turned her pale blue eyes to mine and said, 'you're going to be shocked Maisie, I warn you.' I couldn't think of anything she could have done that would shock me, and I had known her for over fifty years. She was a gentle, very intelligent and well-educated woman who had given so much of her life helping others. More a saint than a sinner, I suggested.

'Just you wait,' she replied, her eyes twinkling with mischief. 'You know that my father was a brilliant pharmacist who spent most of his life trying to find a cure for cancer? He developed many of the drugs that we use today and I wouldn't be surprised if I am taking some of them to help my own breast cancer. It was a tragedy he died so young. He was only 53, you know, and he had a brain tumour. My mother was left a widow for twenty-five years before she died of a stroke when she was seventy-six, so I've outlived them both. They were what I suppose you would call a staid couple. Laughter and exuberant spirits were severely frowned upon, but my father had a wonderfully dry sense of humour that was entirely lacking in my mother, so at least he kept the atmosphere from being too deadly. My mother was a puritan who even thought wearing lipstick was sluttish.'

'But Grannie wasn't like that when we were growing up!'

'No, she mellowed a great deal after my father died, thank goodness. I think she realised that she only had me to look after her as I was her only child - she hated sex, by the way - and that if she wanted a good relationship with me she had to soften her outlook on life and curb her disapproval of everything I did.'

'I don't see how she could have disapproved of anything you did. You've never done anything remotely wicked in your whole life, Mum.'

'That's what you think.'

'What does that mean? Is this the skeleton?'

'Not quite yet. I married your father and she greatly disapproved of him. My father realised straight away that Douglas was a good, ordinary, hard-working man with almost no education, but who had a wonderful brain, and he saw his lack of education and different background as not being your father's fault. And also, quite frankly, I think he was relieved to see me married at last. I was also nearly twenty-four and that was considered bordering on spinsterhood in those days.'

'How ridiculous! I think that twenty-four is almost too *young* to get married.'

'Yes, well, attitudes change. Anyway, my mother was much less forgiving. She was a terrible snob, Maisie, and never, ever, mixed with anyone whom she considered beneath her. It was war from the moment she set eyes on Douglas, and he never forgave her for her cruelty. I'm sorry to say that when she was young my mother had a meanness of spirit. And as I grew into a very attractive young woman she became even meaner, to me anyway, but never to my father. She had a healthy respect for him and his brain, and she adored him, so she was always pleasant to him. Maybe it was because of this that she took out all her jealousy on me. I don't know. Growing up I was very close to my father, we shared the same sense of humour, and I think she saw me as a threat, "the other woman" if you like, and it made her spiteful.'

'Mum! Christ almighty! You were her *own daughter*, how on earth could she treat you as a threat, for God's sake. It's awful!'

'Actually, some mothers find it very difficult when their daughters grow into lovely young women just at the time their own youth and beauty are fading. It's not nearly as uncommon as you might think. My mother was one of those jealous types and I have spent my life trying to forgive her, but sometimes I find it impossible - even though she became so much nicer in her old age, because I think she realised how nasty she had been to me, and tried hard to make up for it. But the deliberate cruelty that was shown to me when I was young is still hard to forgive.'

'I'll say. My kids are vehement about how much hatred they still feel for their birth father.'

'Well, anyway. The only thing that delighted both my parents was dancing. They loved it, and were very good dancers and they used to go to the Assembly Rooms in Newcastle to dance every Saturday night. When I reached seventeen or eighteen, they began to take me with them, and that's where I met Reggie.'

'Reggie? I've never heard of him!'

'I know.'

'So tell me about Reggie.'

'I'm just about to. One Saturday night when we went to the Assembly Rooms there had been a change in the programme and instead of the usual ballroom dancing, it was a jazz night. Naturally my mother heartily disapproved of jazz, she saw it as "black man's music" and found it too sexy and sleazy, so I was taken home immediately, before I could be defiled. But it was too late! I'd already had a taste of it, and instantly loved it. I found it so exciting, and somewhat *daring*. So I began to look out for jazz dancing nights, and Reggie's band in particular. It was called Reggie's Big Jazz Band - not a very original name, I know, and Reggie was the leader and played the saxophone, and sang in a deliciously low, smoky voice. I was hooked, and found every excuse I could to go to listen to Reggie and dance to his music. I lied – I told my parents that I was going to the cinema with a girlfriend - Wendy Nichols, do you remember her? Wendy and I were also taking jazz dancing lessons on Wednesday evenings after work, and soon got pretty good. I was rather attractive in those days and was also a natural dancer like my parents, and very quickly Reggie noticed me and we began to chat between sessions. I fell madly, hopelessly in love with him and we had an affair. I expect that was why I was so sympathetic to Ruth when she fell for Billy. There must be something in our blood that attracted Ruth and me to musicians. Anyway Reggie was my first love and I was such a naive child in those days and knew nothing about contraception, and Reggie didn't take care of me. Pretty quickly I became pregnant and –'

'*Mum!* You've never told me you were pregnant *before* Ruth! Did you have an abortion? What on earth did you do?' Oh my God!'

'I'll tell you if you'll just wait. As I was saying, when I found out I was pregnant and when Reggie didn't offer to marry me, because he said he was not the marrying kind, and having a wife and child would interfere with his music, I realised what a fool I had been. I was in despair, and even considered suicide. It was Wendy who saved me from myself and found me a job in London while I waited for my baby to be born. We lived in grotty digs somewhere behind Earls' Court, and I gave birth all alone in a filthy hospital in the East End, where I felt sure no one would find out, with bombs falling all around. It was a very difficult birth, with a labour that lasted more than twenty-four hours, and I was ripped to shreds. When she was finally born I was told that I had given birth to a mongoloid, as it was called in those days. I was devastated. I was utterly exhausted without a friend in the world except Wendy, and no money. And now I was a single mother with a disabled child and no means of supporting her. What was I to do? The nurses at the hospital were brutal, and told me that I should put my baby in an institution. Mongoloids were considered severely subnormal and uneducable in those days, and parents were made to feel ashamed of their mongoloid children. They tried for days to persuade me to give her up, but I resisted with all my strength. We were in the middle of the war and bombs were being dropped on London every day, *and* there was rationing. I knew it was hopeless, but by the time I was due to leave I had fallen madly in love with my daughter Rose, and was determined no one was going to take her from me. There is no love as fierce and at the same time as tender as the love of a mother for her child, and that love and protection is even stronger if the child is disabled, because it means total dependence. For life. So as soon as they had removed my stitches, I bundled her up in a blanket and sneaked out of the hospital in the dead of night before anyone could stop me. I was not quite nineteen, and babies were not allowed in the digs, of course. Wendy had found me a room in return for cleaning and washing and ironing, and so I lived with Mrs Hilda Smith in her guesthouse in Balham, for over a year. I managed to feed Rose all that time, but it took its toll on my body. I was permanently hungry and exhausted. Hilda was a tough Cockney woman but she had a heart of gold and helped me as much as she could, although she worked me like a donkey.'

Mum's voice had gradually softened as she unfolded her tale and - oh Ruth, how can I explain this too you - her words fell like fine Irish mist, covering us both in tiny droplets of her past and they have clung to my heart ever since, just as fine rain clings to the hairs of a jumper.

For a moment I couldn't speak, then: 'My God, Mum! I never expected anything remotely like this! What a story! What happened to Rose? To think I have another sister and never even knew she existed.'

'I'm coming to it. At the end of the year, I couldn't carry on any longer. I was so tired, and my hair had begun to fall out in handfuls and I was covered in angry red boils. I saved up enough money for a single train fare, packed up my pride and put my few meagre possessions in a battered old suitcase, and took Rose home. And what a homecoming! My mother was so shocked I thought I'd given her a heart attack, and my father didn't speak to me for a year. They did take me in, however, under the condition that I handed Rose over to an institution immediately, and that I never visit her, or even mention her name again. It was a dark, shameful secret that no one must *ever*, under *any circumstances*, find out. I knew I had no choice, but it was agony. And what sort of life would she have had in that frozen atmosphere? So I took my baby to a long-stay hospital after dark, weeping copiously all the way, and left her there. It broke my heart. And there she stayed until she died. She only lived until she was ten. Life expectancy for people with Down's was low in the 1940's, it wasn't like now, when they can live until they're in their sixties, go to school, and have fairly normal lives, thank God. What a cruel world it was! At least there have been some improvements since I was young, but I never saw her again.'

'What did she look like? Do you have a photo of her?'

'No, I regret I don't. I wasn't in a position to pay to have her photo taken and of course I didn't own a camera. She was a peach, Maisie, with bright blue eyes and a shock of chestnut hair and a tiny, turned-up nose. Quite lovely.'

This was such a strong and unexpected tale, and its poignancy caused tears to roll gently down my face as I listened. Our poor mother - what she had suffered at the hands of her awful parents. And we complain about Dad, Ruth, but he looks almost kind in comparison to our grandparents.

'Don't cry, darling. It all happened a very long time ago. But of course it was such an unhappy episode in my life that I have never wanted to relive it. My parents made me feel so ashamed. At every opportunity they made it very clear to me that I was damaged goods and would probably never find a husband, and even though no one knew about Rose, they lived in dread that my "wicked secret" as they called it, would be discovered. If I had been a prostitute they could not have been more scathing and disgusted. Now it seems as if it were another person that all these things had happened to. But it was a lifetime ago.'

'Does Dad know all about it?'

'Of course he does. Let me tell you what happened next. I was living with my parents but my home had become a prison. I was not allowed to go out and I spent every evening alone, reading in my room. It was like living under the Stasi. But I managed to get into Newcastle University to read English literature and that gave me some relief, spending the day with young people and even learning to laugh again; but I had to go home every evening. Of course I couldn't tell my friends why I went home every night and why I never joined them at the university bar in the evenings. I acquired a reputation for being a blue stocking, but this suited me, as it didn't require my having to explain my past to anyone. Just to get out of the house at the weekend, I worked as a volunteer in a hospital, which is why I have such a phobia of hospitals now, I think! Anyway, one day in my last few weeks at University, your father was brought in on a stretcher. He had had a terrible accident at one of his building sites and had broken his arm in several places, as well as some of his ribs. His face was covered in blood, and because I was well known in the hospital by then and they were very short staffed, they asked me if I could take him into a cubicle and clean him up while he waited to be seen by the doctor. He had been lying very still with his eyes closed, and as I began to gently wash his cuts, he opened them and looked up at me leaning over him and asked, "Have I died, and are you an angel?" Of course I had had plenty of time to study him, and he was a very handsome man in his youth. Michael looks just like him, except much taller. Dad had jet-black hair and dark brown eyes, when they finally opened, and was tanned and very strong. His mouth was full and soft, and his straight nose gave him a wonderful profile.'

'It sounds as if you fell in love at first sight, Mum.'

'Perhaps. I was struck by him, it's true. There was something so alive, so penetrating in his gaze, as if he knew all about me and didn't care.'

'Wow!'

'I jumped up to call the nurse, but he grabbed hold of my wrist with his left hand and said 'Please don't leave me, angel.'

'I should get the nurse. I think you'll need stitches, now I can see what's under the blood and dirt,' I told him.

'Promise you'll come straight back?' he pleaded. And of course I promised I would.

Days passed by and at his request I visited him whenever I could on my way home from university. On one of those evenings his mother and his sister had come to visit him. They were lovely people, Maisie, so kind and simple and the contrast between our parents was brought into sharp focus. They gazed at Douglas with such love in their eyes it made me want to cry. They were sitting on either side of the bed, each holding one of his hands and they looked up at me with open kindness.

'Ah! Here comes my guardian angel I've been telling you about!' Douglas announced. 'Margaret, this is my mother Amy, and my sister Lyn.'

Two pairs of shy, but curious eyes looked into mine, as I went forward to shake their hands.

'Douglas has been telling us how kind you've been to him

while he's been in hospital. Thank you very much, dear. We live in Tynemouth and it's quite a journey on the bus, isn't it, Lyn, so we can't come as often as we'd like, so I'm glad he has a friend to visit him.'

Gradually I met the whole family as his brothers came in together one weekend when they could get away from work at the shipyard. They were all simple, good people and I relaxed in their company in a way I never had in my own home.

As soon as he was well enough Douglas asked me if I would visit him at his home while he was recuperating. It was over these few weeks that we really got to know one another and I suppose we fell in love.'

'What do you mean, "I suppose we fell in love". Surely you know if you have or not?'

'It's difficult to explain, Maisie. I'd been badly bruised emotionally and I didn't trust men any more. I'd worked my way through university and had just got my first job teaching English Literature in a school in Jesmond, and had decided to move into a flat nearby. My parents could do nothing about it. After all, I was twenty-three or twenty-four and earning my own living and, actually, I think they were probably as relieved to get away from me as I was to leave them. At long last I had my freedom and independence, and I didn't want to lose it by getting involved with another man, however much I was attracted to him. Do you see?'

'Yes, I understand now.'

'I was prepared to go out with him once or twice a week, but no more. Douglas respected my reasons and so that's what we did for over a year. Gradually I learnt to trust him and eventually I told him my story, and do you know what he did when I had finished? He laughed! It had taken me a year to pluck up courage to tell him and

I could have actually hit him at that moment, I was so furious, demanding to know what on earth he could find amusing in my tragedy.

'It's just this, Margaret' he said. 'Where I come from so many girls find themselves in the family way. Although it's not approved of, these pregnancies take place all the time in Tynemouth and you wouldn't credit how many "sisters and brothers" or "nieces and nephews" suddenly appear in families where the mothers are long past the age of conceiving. Families in poor areas band together and help each other in times of need, not because they're more altruistic than the rich, but simply because they have to. What your parents did to you was appalling; I don't know how you can ever forgive them.' He was extremely sympathetic and didn't give two hoots that I was not a virgin and had had a child. 'I'm not a virgin either!' was his only comment and so, after a year, I took him to meet my parents. I had prepared them, of course, and told them a little about Douglas, what a fine man he was and how he had kept his family since he was fourteen years old, but this did not impress your grandmother. She was icy towards him all evening, barely opening her mouth, and I hated her for it. She had no right to make another human being feel so uncomfortable and unwelcome in her home. At the door, when we said goodbye - I had to stay to wash up of course, before I could go back to my own flat - I apologised to him for her behaviour.

"That's OK, angel," he said magnanimously. "I've met them now, and I won't hurry to repeat the experience!" And he didn't, not until our wedding. And even though Douglas was working class, I think they were relieved when we were married, because as they saw it, I became someone else's problem. As you know, Douglas is able to completely ignore what he doesn't like. It's probably what saved him as a child. If one takes every slight deeply, it can hinder one from getting on in life. Too much unnecessary baggage I think you would call it, Maisie. And of course, we were the generation of the stiff upper lip. And in war and times of great hardship and deprivation, any sign of self pity was deeply frowned upon.'

By now Mum was exhausted, so I left her to rest and went home, my mind whirling with everything I had heard. It's quite a story, isn't it, Ruth? I wonder what you will make of it when you read it. I have typed up all of her notes about her life as she gradually told them to the tape recorder, but nothing was as dramatic as this story and as she had said, most of the other family stories I knew already.

With very much love,

Maisie

From: Ruth Braydon ruthbraydon@cedaw.com.ar
Date: 16th April 2011
To: Maisie Wilton maisiewilton@btinternet.com

Dear Maisie,

I wish our mother had told us the story of her Down's syndrome child years ago. Although it was immensely poignant, I also felt irrationally hurt, even cheated somehow, that she hadn't trusted us with it before. Why didn't she? Did she offer any explanation other than she didn't want to relive it, because it had been such a ghastly experience? Did you feel hurt at all? Am I being ridiculous at my age to feel like a rejected child again, just because my mother withheld something important from her past? More than likely I am, and it is interesting to note these old feelings as they float unbidden to the surface of my consciousness.

It is the same old hurt that I still carry and have mentioned to you before. To me, this story only illustrates further her lack of openness with me. We all protected you from Dad, but she never tried to protect me, and what I couldn't stand was that she wouldn't even talk to me about it!

Ah well, I will put my childish sensibilities back in the bottom of the box where they belong, and remember just how much I hurt her.

Much love,

Ruth

From: Maisie Wilton maisiewilton@btinternet.com
Date: 17th April 2011
To: Ruth Braydon ruthbraydon@cedaw.com.ar

Dear Ruth,

In the nicest possible way – grow up! I thought you prided yourself on not being a whinger? Your endless complaints about Mum not standing up for us or being open with you are really getting on my nerves. And you were a very difficult teenager, you might care to remember. Argumentative and punchy, although I know now that some of those fights with Dad were for my benefit. Mike and I used to call you 'Ruthless Ruth', but now I think we might refer to you as 'Reckless Ruth'. I've already said several times how sad it made me that you and Mum had an awkward love/hate relationship, but your complaints have become just plain irritating. You were quite capable of standing up for yourself, and you always did. Particularly when you wanted to run off with Fernando. Ever consider how *your* children feel about their mother?

And it's really hurtful for me to hear you talking about Mum like that when she's only been dead five months. I miss her dreadfully, and not a day goes by without my thinking of her. You haven't seen her, or any of us, for so long, I think you have become extremely detached from everyone. That's the main reason I have made such an enormous effort and taken so much time to fill you in, so that you do get the full picture. Otherwise how would you know?

So do you want me to continue revealing the past, or shall I edit everything? Because I am just about to get back to Ricky, and as I have already warned you, it will not make pleasant reading.

Up to you, Ruthie. And if I were you, I'd burn that bloody box!

Love

Maisie

From: Ruth Braydon ruthbraydon@cedaw.com.ar
Date: 21st April 2011
To: Maisie Wilton maisiewilton@btinternet.com

Dear Maisie,

Points taken on all fronts. I haven't got a leg to stand on, have I?
But you are right; I am behaving like a spoilt child. And I'm very
sorry I hurt you complaining about Mum. I apologize, and I'd
like you to know I have figuratively already eaten several humble
pies!

Please do not leave *anything out*, and I promise I'll stop complaining. At *last* we are getting to Ricky. But please hurry, because I might have to go away soon and I really, desperately, want
to hear it all before I leave.

With lots of love,

Yours in humility!

Ruth

From: Maisie Wilton maisiewilton@btinternet.com
Date: 23rd April 2011
To: Ruth Braydon ruthbraydon@cedaw.com.ar

Dear Ruth,

Apologies accepted. I'll get on with the story as quickly as I can then, as you are going away soon. Where are you going? Anywhere nice? And is it for work, or on holiday?

You'll remember that I got as far as discovering that Ricky was drinking a huge amount of alcohol and had moved in with us. Unbeknownst to me, he had been attending school less and less, and Mr Adams, his headmaster, had rung me to tell me that they could do no more and that Ricky had been expelled.

And so to continue:

When Tommy came home that day I asked him if he would come straight upstairs to our bedroom as I needed to talk to him. Our bedroom was the only room in the house where we could find a little privacy, when all the children were still living at home.

'You'd better lock the door Tommy. I don't want to be interrupted.'

'This is serious then?'

'Yes. Ricky hasn't been going to school as we thought. Mr Adams rang this morning and expelled him. They've tried their best, he said, but he's a lost cause. Whatever is he going to do? He's only seventeen with a dozen good 'GCSE's but only poor 'AS' levels and no future at all.'

'Maisie, most people have good lives with far fewer qualifications than that! You grew up with your father telling you exactly that every single day! Ricky's a very bright boy and I'm sure he'll find a way. Perhaps it's all for the best. There is no point forcing him to go to school if he doesn't want to.'

'But what's he going to *do*, Tommy? He has to have a reason to get up in the morning, and although he has his allowance from Billy, it's not healthy to hang about aimlessly all day. I've been racking my brains since this morning, and I haven't come up with anything.'

'Is he home yet?'

'No.'

'Well let's wait till he comes home and then ask him if he has any ideas. He might surprise us.'

'Seems sensible. Who knows, he might even be relieved that this has happened. But what on earth has he been doing all day long?'

'We'll ask him that, too.'

Ricky didn't come home until just before dinner, so we had to wait until we had eaten and cleared the dishes before asking him to come upstairs to our room.

'But I'm going out!' he cried in amazement, clearly annoyed at this interruption to his evening.

'No you're not. Not until we've had a talk,' said Tommy.

Ricky stomped up the stairs making his fury and frustration obvious.

'What's the big deal?' he asked as he thumped down on our bed.

'You've been expelled from school, Ricky. Mr Adams rang Maisie this morning and told her that they'd tried their best, but you were hardly ever there.'

'Is that all?' laughed Ricky. 'I thought this was something serious! It took them long enough to notice, stupid gits.'

'This is *extremely* serious, Ricky. It means that university is out of the question and you must think very hard about your future. You'll have to get a job, of course. Do you have any ideas?'

'Not really, except I thought that if I took my driving test I could probably get work as a driver.'

'Actually, that's not such a bad idea. You should take your test anyway. And it would help Maisie enormously if you could take the girls to school in the morning.'

'Are you not at all sorry to have left school, Ricky?' I asked. I just *had* to know how he really felt about no longer being able to go to university.

'You must be kidding, Maisie! I hated that place and anyway I've grown out of school and education. I just want to earn my own living and live my own life, not under stupid petty school rules.'

'But what've you been doing all day these past few months?'

'Just hanging out, with my mates. That's all. Trying to make a few quid here and there. Nothing to get stressed about, promise.'

'But will you be sorry later? That you didn't get a degree, I mean?'

'He can always go to university later on, Maisie,' Tommy answered for him.

'Yeah, right. So can I go now?'

'Yes, you may. But I want you up in the morning and learning your driving theory.'

'Will do!' And he smiled his sweet, cheeky smile, and I really thought that it might be all right after all.

Ricky was extremely keen to pass his test and worked hard at his theory and passed first time. I bought some L plates and he drove me everywhere until he passed his test. He was a natural driver and took to it like a duck to water. He was so keen to pass that he didn't stay out as late as he had been doing, and he didn't go out at all the night before his test. I clung to this ray of hope and hoped that he might be turning a corner, but he told me years later it was only because he didn't want to be breathalysed.

The minute he passed his test he was off like greased lightening. He bought a second hand Renault Clio with your money, Ruth, and went out in it all day. I didn't know what he was up to and when I asked, he said he was working as a mini cab driver and was making quite a bit of money. That seemed fine to me, although he didn't have his Hackney Carriage licence, but when I mentioned it to him he just brushed me aside and said that no one bothered with that these days, and it wasn't a problem. So we let him continue, believing every word he told us, and he did seem to have quite a bit of cash on him, all of a sudden. What he was really doing Ruth, was driving down to the docks to collect drugs when the shipment arrived, and delivering them to the dealers up and down the coast. He was paid in cocaine and cash, and was quite well off for a while, but he quickly became addicted to cocaine.

But we didn't know anything about it then, and actually spent a few weeks in blissful ignorance. Then one night, at three in the morning, the phone rang.

'Mrs Wilton?'

'Speaking. Who is it?'

'This is Dr Chandler from the R.V.I. I'm afraid your nephew has been in an accident and is quite badly hurt. He had a car crash and was driving while he was considerably over the limit.

The police found him, but I think it would be wise if you came down straight away.'

'Oh my God! How badly hurt is he?'

'He hit his head on the windscreen and will need treatment. He was also concussed for a moment or two, we think. We'll have to do a brain scan in the morning to see if there are any head injuries, and until we have the results there's not much more I can tell you, I'm afraid. But because he is still under eighteen, I need you to sign a consent form giving me permission to carry out any necessary treatment, in case he needs surgery. Could you come over straight away, please? I'm sorry to ask you to come in the middle of the night, but we don't know at this stage what damage he has done, and we might need to move quickly.'

'I'm on my way' I said, and jumped out of bed, my heart stuck in my throat like a boulder.

'What's happened, Maisie?' Tommy asked, instantly alert and wide awake.

'It's Ricky. He's had a car crash and was way over the limit. I need to go to the R.V.I. immediately to sign a consent form, because he's still under eighteen. Oh *God*, Tommy! He's only had his licence for six weeks, and seemed to be doing so well. This will really put him back.'

'I'll come with you, Maisie.'

'*No.* You need your sleep, and we can't both leave the girls alone in the middle of the night. They might wake up and be terrified that we'd deserted them.'

'You're right. But please call me as soon as you can. I won't be able to go back to sleep now, I'm sure.'

Ricky looked awful. He had a large open gash across the middle of his forehead and he was covered in blood, lying on a bed in intensive care. They had been too busy that night to clean him up. He managed a weak smile when he saw me, and his eyes filled with tears.

'I'm here, Ricky. It's O.K. You're going to be fine, darling,' I said, although my voice did the lying for me. The nurse looked up at me and smiled as she checked his drips. I was so grateful for that small kindness.

'Lost my licence, Maisie. The police found me.'

'So I gather. But you're not the first young man to go mad as soon as you get behind the wheel of a car. You'll just have to take the test again. Thank God you didn't kill yourself, or anyone else for that matter.'

'But I've got to go to court.'

'Don't worry, I'll come with you. But don't think about that now. Just get some rest and we'll deal with it all in the morning.'

'Thanks for coming Maisie.'

He sounded like the old Ricky, the sweet boy he had always been before the family drama but as I looked down at him I saw the frightened expression of a small boy who had done something unforgivable.

'Would you like me to sit with you, Ricky? That is, if I'm allowed?' I turned and looked enquiringly at the nurse, who nodded.

'We don't usually allow anyone in intensive care at this time of night, but it's relatively quiet at the moment, so it's O.K. to stay for a while.'

I thanked her and pulled up a chair next to Ricky and held his hand in mine as he drifted off to sleep.

The head scan was clear and showed that there were no fractures or internal bleeding, and after a couple days in hospital, I went to collect him and brought him home. He was left with a thin jagged scar that stretched from his hairline down between his eyebrows, and the girls laughed and called it his 'Harry Potter scar.' Years later he said it was his first war wound; there were many other accidents to follow.

Ruth, its seven o'clock and I have to stop now to make dinner. It's suddenly got cold again – we're having a late spring cold snap - and I'm really worried that it will kill off my roses, which are just coming into leaf. I made a large pot of stock this morning to make a thick northern Italian minestrone soup for tonight, and I haven't even started. It might be a few days before I can continue. I've an appointment with Mum's solicitor tomorrow and various other things to do which involve chasing around for lost documents and so on, but I will get back to you shortly.

With much love,

Maisie

From: Ruth Braydon ruthbraydon@cedaw.com.ar
Date: 24th April 2011
To: Maisie Wilton maisiewilton@btinternet.com

Dear Maisie,

I know that life must go on, but please hurry to continue! I will have to go away quite soon and where I'm going there is no email, and of course I am living every day longing to know the end before I have to leave. The waiting at my side is agony, but of course, I am having a real taste of my own medicine. As each day passes with no news from you it is as if I am forced to suffer in exactly the same way I made my own family suffer.

Again, I must tell you how very sorry I am that you had to deal with it all. You must have hated me. I hope you don't any more.

And to think he became a drug courier and was taking cocaine! I could *murder* those men who put him up to it. And he had such a bright future. I naturally expected him to go to university; as you said, he had been such a good student.

But I will cling to the reassurance that he is all right now with all my remaining strength, but it is hard to imagine how he could be.

Your loving sister,

Ruth

From: Maisie Wilton maisiewilton@btinternet.com
Date: 27th April 2011
To: Ruth Braydon ruthbraydon@cedaw.com.ar

Dear Ruth,

OK. I'll just get straight into it. I *do* sympathise with you, really. Believe me, we know all about waiting in agony, and this time I'm not referring to you! And of course I don't hate you, Ruth. Although I'll confess that many times I wished I could have shared the burden with you and Mike. Anyway, to continue:

As soon as he was fit enough, he started leaving the house again. At first he told us that he had got a job in a bakery, then a job in a newsagent, in Wallsend. Both jobs required him to be at work at five in the morning he said, and he told us he'd be better off renting a small room nearby. It seemed sensible, as he had been banned from driving for eighteen months, and he started work before the first bus ran. His car was a write-off and when I saw it a few days later, I almost passed out.

'He's a very lucky boy,' said the mechanic. 'I wonder how he got out of that alive. Drunk, was he?'

I nodded in shame.

'They always are. Not the first, and I dare say not the last, unfortunately. Seen too many of these crashes for my liking. I'll let the insurance company know it's a write-off and they'll get in touch with you in due course.' And he turned on his heel and left me.

We only saw Ricky two or three times for over a year. I asked him over every weekend, but he was always busy with his friends, he said, and I thought that at eighteen, it was normal. The only question at the back of my mind was that he would never give me his address. Each time he evaded it, and so our only point of contact was through his mobile, which went straight to his messaging service and it was always days before he returned my calls - and more often than not, he didn't return them at all. I deeply regret I left him to his own devices for so long, but no sooner had he left hospital and moved to Wallsend, Mum fell and broke her hip, and my time was consumed with caring for her. I was beginning to feel as if I lived in a hospital.

The next time we saw him was on his nineteenth birthday. I wanted to give him a family meal and some presents and was surprised, and even a little hurt, when he was initially reluctant to come.

'You don't have to do anything for me, Maisie. I'm fine.'

'But I *want* to, Ricky. Please come. After all it isn't your birthday every day. What would you like to eat?'

'I dunno. Whatever you think. Roast chicken and fried potatoes?'

'O.K. And I'll buy a bottle of champagne and we'll have a jolly time, all together. It's been ages since we've seen you, and I miss you.'

With hindsight, I now see that he arrived as late as possible and left as soon as he could. I was beginning to think that maybe he wouldn't come at all, when the door opened and he shouted 'Hello!' He was high, but I didn't know it then, I thought it was just youthful high spirits and after all, it was his birthday, and I was glad to see him so happy. We opened the champagne and Alec and the girls gave him his presents, and the girls watched with fierce concentration as he opened them to see if he really liked the gifts they had chosen, with so much love and care.

'Wow! A CD of my favourite band! Thanks Joy, you're a poppet.'

Joy squirmed with pleasure and pride and hung around his neck while he opened all his other presents. There was a card from Billy but no gift, and nothing at all from you, Ruth. We didn't mention it but I know he must have felt it. And not mentioning it only made it more obvious. Jane had bought him a new CD player and a laptop, and I thought it was as if she felt she had to compensate for the lack of presents from their parents, but he was very happy and grateful. I did notice that he drank much faster and much more than anyone else and seemed - how shall I put it - almost *excessively* happy? Does that make sense? He kept disappearing to the loo, and I asked him if he had a cold, because he sniffed all the time, but his eyes looked very bright, and he laughed and said it was only a sniffle, and I accepted it.

He hugged Jane and asked her all about her life and her work in the hospital. I watched them together with joy, naively unaware that it was all a ruse to draw attention away from *him*. He didn't want anyone asking him awkward questions. I thought what a lovely boy he was underneath all that anger and turmoil, and of course he *is* a nice boy, Ruth. Being an addict doesn't mean you are a bad *person*. An addict is just an ordinary person with an illness. After all, one wouldn't dream of accusing someone with cancer of being a *bad person*. But I'm often surprised the way society views addiction, although generally speaking, we're all much better informed than we used to be. Addiction is either glamorised or demonised, and neither is real. One can be addicted to food. Think of those sad obese people, stuffing themselves with hamburgers and a double portion of fries, on their way home to dinner. Or women who can't stop shopping, buying hundreds of expensive handbags and designer dresses they can't possibly afford. And what about shopaholic *men,* who buy dozens of watches which they never wear, and cars and speedboats, and endless gizmos, which are thrown in a drawer and which they never even learn to use? Drugs and alcohol certainly aren't the only substances to which one can become addicted; one can become addicted to *anything.* Gambling, and even *sex,* for heaven's sake, like Michael Douglas. I wonder how Catherine Zeta-Jones coped with *that*? The truth is that it takes superhuman courage and strength of character to get clean and sober, and even greater strength to remain so. Some of the finest people I have ever had the privilege of knowing are in recovery. There is honesty and a self awareness that comes from living the Twelve Steps that few ordinary mortals achieve. People in recovery know the meaning of living in the moment like no others.

Jane had passed her nursing finals with top marks, and was working in the geriatric ward which she said was pretty ghastly. She had us all roaring with laughter with tales of the poor old people in the ward, and I hadn't felt so happy and relaxed for a long time. Ricky even asked Alec how his course was going at university. They had almost nothing in common, and had not become any closer while Ricky had lived with us. Ricky found Alec boring. Alec was naturally quiet and serious, but sweet and solid as a rock. When Ricky called Alec "a sad fuck" Alec just laughed and we all joined in with good humour.

'When I make my millions I expect I'll need an accountant so you might come in useful after all, you never know! But I don't intend to pay any tax, if I can avoid it!'

I served a homemade ice cream bomb, and Joy helped me light the sparklers on the top. They fizzled along with atmosphere, and Tommy opened another bottle of Champagne to go with the dessert. We were all getting very merry, so it was a shock when the doorbell rang not long after nine, and Ricky jumped to his feet and said,

'Gotta go. That'll be my lift. Bye everyone, and thanks for the lovely meal and all the presents!' We hardly had time to say good-bye before he rushed out of the house and went speeding away in a battered white van. We were left sitting around the table feeling rather deflated, and a little sad. Ricky had gone, and had taken all the fun with him.

'Who on earth's he gone off with?' I asked Jane at last.

'I've no idea, but I expect he has an early start in the morning. Didn't he say he has to be at the newsagents at 5a.m.? Let me help you clear up, Maisie. It's been a wonderful party, thank you so much.'

Ricky had been banned from driving for eighteen months, and the minute his licence was returned to him, he bought another car, and carried on with his life as a courier. But things didn't work out so well for him the second time around, and he had a row with one of the drug bosses who accused him of stealing cocaine for his own use, which of course, he had been doing, and he was cast out with the threat of a painful death hanging over him if he ever told anyone. He had no money, and nowhere to live, and was addicted to alcohol and cocaine. He sold his car, his CD player and new laptop, but that money didn't last long and he went for weeks surviving on left-overs from the city bins, and soup kitchens. He began to steal, and had been living rough, but when it got too cold to sleep outside, he moved back to Newcastle, and started to sleep in our garden shed. He'd creep in after dark, and stay there until we had all left in the morning, then he would let himself into the house, and take whatever money and drink he found lying around. He stole my credit card and withdrew £1,000 before I noticed. He fed himself from the fridge, but as he cleverly never finished anything, we all assumed it was one of us who had eaten half the cheese, or most of the eggs and bread. None of us noticed - we were living rather chaotically I suppose - and had always been very casual about leaving our cash around. Again, we were unaware of all of this until I had a call from Newcastle Central Police Station on Friday afternoon.

'I have your nephew at the station, Mrs Wilton,' I was told without ceremony. 'He's been charged with theft, and unless you are prepared to bail him out, he'll have to go into custody until he is sentenced.'

'I see. How much is the bail?'

'Near enough five hundred pounds. It's not as much he could have been charged, because he only stole a watch.'

'Where did he take it from?'

'The jewellery counter in Fenwicks. He was spotted on their CCTV, and the store guard caught him on the way out. But he put up quite a fight, so I hope he doesn't get done for assault as well.'

'Oh my God! Did he hurt him?'

'Not too badly. The guard's got quite a bruise, so you'll just have to hope he doesn't press charges. But the court takes assault extremely seriously these days. That's why the bail is so high'.

'Five hundred pounds! I don't suppose the watch was worth half that!'

'That's not the point Mrs Wilton, as I'm sure you'll agree.'

'Of course. I'm sorry. When shall I come?'

'As soon as you can. We've all the paperwork to do beforehand, but if he's a lucky lad, he won't have to stay in overnight.'

I went straight to the bank and took out the money in cash. Then I phoned Tommy and said that I might be late home and asked if he would he look after the girls and make them all dinner. I had to tell him that Ricky was in trouble again, but managed not to say exactly what kind of trouble, only it was nothing to do with alcohol.

When I arrived at the station, I was shown into a small room with only one table and a single chair. There was a tiny window high up in the corner of the wall covered with metal bars, and the only light came from a weak bare bulb hanging high above the table. The room was cold and the air smelt stale and dead, as if it had been reused for years. I waited for nearly an hour becoming increasingly claustrophobic and depressed, before Ricky was brought into the room, his face hanging, his eyes fixed firmly on his boots.

I leapt up to hug him and he let me, but he didn't hug me back.

'Are you O.K., Ricky?' I asked.

'Just about.'

'What's happened to you? Why did you steal a watch, for goodness' sake? You've plenty of money of your own and a job! Whatever made you do it, Ricky?'

'I dunno. I just did. That's all.'

The duty officer came in, and looked at me very seriously.

'He's allowed out on bail and will be charged at the magistrates' court next Wednesday. Here are his belongings.' And he passed me a plastic bag with Ricky's mobile, belt and wallet.

'As he's no longer a minor, he'll run the risk of being sent down for a term. A pity. He's just turned twenty, hasn't he? The remand centre is certainly a better option than prison, but he's missed the boat. You can only hope that the magistrate will be extremely generous to you, as it's already your second offence lad. That's all I can say. You're free to go now, but behave yourself. I warn you, be at the magistrates' court if it's the *last thing you do*. Get it?' Ricky nodded and, shaken, we walked out into the busy evening streets of Newcastle, towards my car.

When we got home, Ricky went straight up to his room and shut the door. I suggested that he do that as I could see how difficult it would be to face the family until I had had time to discuss it with Tommy, and work out what we were going to say to the girls. I didn't want them to know, and worry. They all adored Ricky because he was such a live wire, and made them laugh so much, when he was on good form. Once we had all eaten and the girls had gone to do their homework and watch TV, I closed the kitchen door and told Tommy.

'Whatever's got into him? That's not like Ricky, is it? I mean he's had his fair share of problems, but he shouldn't need to steal. He's got a job hasn't he?'

'I know. That's what I don't understand, and he won't talk about it. The only thing he did mention was that he sold his car, but wouldn't say why. When I pressed him, because he had been so happy to have his licence back, he just said that he lived too close to work to need it. Tommy, do you think there is something else going on? Could he have got a girl pregnant, or something like that?'

'I've no idea. But he must be terrified by the possibility of prison. I'll take him some food up to his room and have a chat, and see if I can find out anything more.'

But Tommy didn't find out anything new. Ricky was very pale

and quiet, shaking with cold, or so we thought. So Tommy suggested that he have a hot bath and a good night's sleep, and we'd talk it over in the morning.

But when the morning came, Tommy and the girls had already left before Ricky came downstairs. We had decided that sleep was probably what he needed more than anything, and so we hadn't woken him. He looked a lot better when he finally woke, and I made him a huge breakfast of bacon and eggs and toast. He ate like a starving man, asking for more and more toast. He stayed at home for five days before he went up in front of the magistrate, and it was the only five days he was clean and sober in years. I took him to the hairdresser before he went, and he was cleanly shaven, and dressed nicely. He borrowed a grey suit from Tommy, and a shirt and tie, and I hadn't seen him look so smart and neat since he was a schoolboy. He looked such a beautiful innocent as I watched him standing in the dock, and I think it helped him, because he got off with a large fine and community service, and was bound over to keep the peace for a year.

'Thank God that's over!' I almost shouted in relief, as we whipped our way home. 'That's my second time in court with you, young man. Can you please make sure it is my last?'

'Will do, Maisie! And thanks so much for coming with me, and for paying for my fine, and bail. Now, if you don't mind, as soon as we get home, I'll be on my way.'

'Whatever do you mean, on your way? On your way where, for goodness sake?'

'Back to my job at the newsagent, of course! I rang them and told them I had flu and they let me have a week off, but I must go back to work today.'

And "sad fuck" as Ricky would have called me, I believed him.

That's all I can manage in this letter, Ruth. I will continue as soon as possible, as I know that you are waiting. Waiting, and not knowing, is awful. I do understand. I have done too much waiting in the past few years. So until the next letter, farewell!

Your loving sister,

Maisie

From: Ruth Braydon ruthbraydon@cedaw.com.ar
Date: 1st May 2011
To: Maisie Wilton maisiewilton@btinternet.com

Dear Maisie,

In your latest email Ricky has written off his car driving when drunk, been working as a drug runner, or whatever it is called, been caught stealing a watch and has been in front of the magistrate twice! And he is a drug addict and an alcoholic! And there was I, telling you, *you* of all people, who have had to deal with this on a daily basis, that a bit of pot smoking was just a rite of passage. My God, Maisie! How you must have *hated* me when you read that stupid email of mine. No wonder you took umbrage! Please forgive me. Forgive my ignorance and my jumping to conclusions. I had no idea, of course. Absolutely no inkling.

I know there is no use in crying over spilt milk, but my tears would not be controlled. I am putting all my strength into taking heart, because you said, indeed you have *assured* me more than once, that there *is* a happy ending. I can't image how, nor how Ricky will come out of all this mess, but I do need to know. I need to know it all, Maisie, however taxing it is for you having to relive it in your memory as you commit it all to paper.

And all this dreadful business going on while Mum was in hospital with a broken hip, and then diagnosed with breast cancer and Parkinson's, and you and Tommy caring for her afterwards and searching for a carer. It is hard for me to imagine how you survived it all, Maisie. It must have been terrible, because it is still so painful for you to relive it. *And* you had your own four children to look after! You have such a deep well of inner strength, Maisie, which I confess I was unaware of until now. And Tommy, too.

But seriously, never in a *million years* did I dream that my departure would have such a devastating effect on Ricky! Surely that reaction is not normal? You tell me. After all, you're the one with foster children who came from a very disturbed background. And both you and Tommy are special needs teachers. You're the experts in all this, not me. Tell me if I'm wrong, but I just find Ricky's behaviour to be so extraordinary. So extreme. What if I had died, for example? Would he have fallen apart in the same way? I think it would have been better if I *had* died. Then there would have been a reason for my absence. A reason that everyone could accept. And while I'm on the subject, how did Dad take my departure? And Mum? You've never mentioned it. I'm sorry that I asked you to tell them, but I had no option. Mike was in Australia, and it all happened so quickly. I'd like to know. I think. Although I'm not sure how much more bad news I can take.

I did like the way you explained addiction. I had no idea that it was an actual *illness*. Is that what you meant when you said back in January that he had been ill? I had always seen addiction as an inner weakness that a strong character should, and could, control. What I don't understand is *how* one becomes an addict in the first place? It's easier to understand becoming addicted to drugs. I know that some can be addictive from the first hit. But alcohol? Doesn't that take years and years of heavy drinking first? And Ricky was *so young.* There's none of this anywhere else in our family is there? So where does it come from? I suppose Dad is extreme, and also bloody minded, but he's not an addictive personality, is he? And Billy most certainly is not! Just the opposite! It's funny, in a tragic way, to think that there was Billy, mixing with all those drinking and drug taking rock stars, and only wanting to be at home with his family and a cup of tea, and yet his son, our son, our beautiful, football playing, *normal* son, should turn out like this. I'm afraid I *don't* understand, Maisie. Nor will I take the blame for his 'illness.' It may very well be an illness, but I cannot see how it is a direct result of my leaving home. What about families whose marriage ends in divorce? Very often the fathers do not see their children ever again, or so I hear. And don't tell me all those children end up on drugs, for goodness sake!

No doubt I've put my foot in it again. So please don't be angry with me Maisie, I'm only trying to make sense of it all. It is very difficult, from such a great distance, in both time and mileage, to understand, that's all. I'm asking all these questions because you seem to have become quite an expert on the subject, mores the pity. I stand to be corrected on any point you know, and before I make any more unforgivable blunders, I'll finish now.

Your loving and *extremely grateful* sister,

Ruth

From: Maisie Wilton maisiewilton@btinternet.com
Date: 4th May 2011
To: Ruth Braydon ruthbraydon@cedaw.com.ar

My dear Ruth,

It's O.K. I realise it was your shock and pain talking. And in an odd sort of way, it was easier for Tommy and me because it all happened gradually, drip by drip, day after day, year after year, not in a few dramatic chunks, as you have received it.

As for my being an expert, well, I certainly know a great deal more about addiction than I did a few years ago, but it was a steep learning curve for me, too. And not only in addiction, but also about breast cancer and Parkinson's and caring for the elderly and infirm, and so on. But these are just the things that happen in old age. No doubt it will come to us all, eventually. That inevitable role reversal, the parent becoming the child, and the child, the parent.

You asked if there is any addiction within our family. I do not believe there is and of course it's too late to ask Mum now. So many times I have wondered about our family and have had the urge to ask her something, and now I can't. She was always the first person I would telephone with good news, and the first person to whom I would turn for advice, after Tommy. So many times since she died I've longed to pick up the phone to tell her something, and not being able to has brought the heartfelt loss of her home to me all over again. She was the family keeper of secrets, the only one who knew our family history on both sides, and I wish I had paid more attention when she was alive. Such regrets! But my friends whose mothers have also died have told me it is exactly the same for them.

And as for blame, what can I say? We are all lonely souls who must cope with loss and hardship in our own, individual way. Maybe Ricky would have been an addict even if you had not fled. As you so rightly say, not all children of divorced families become addicts. The whys and wherefores are outside my knowledge. You need to speak to a psychiatrist for those answers. Why not write and ask Mike's son, Bruce? He is a fully qualified behavioural psychiatrist, and specialises in drug and alcohol abuse, so he should have most of the answers.

You also asked me to tell you about how Mum and Dad received the news of your departure. With incredulity, followed by outright fury, from Dad. Of course it was utterly ghastly, as you would expect, and really Ruth, I haven't the energy to repeat that hideous afternoon, there is enough far tougher stuff I have to write about first. If you *still* want to know once I have finished the saga, then I will tell you. But for the moment, I will continue to tell you about your son.

So Ricky disappeared from our life once more, and went back to Wallsend to work - at least that's what we thought. He immediately sold Tommy's suit, shirt and tie, and even his black leather shoes, but his habit cost him far more than his allowance afforded. Of course he had never had a job in a bakery or a newsagent. He had found a much more effective way to earn a living to feed his habit. He became a rent boy. I did warn you it wasn't going to be nice, Ruth.

He had been hanging around the docks at Tynemouth hoping to beg a few quid and as he had had little luck, he ended up walking towards the men's public lavatories not far from the beach. It was winter and he was blue with cold and he huddled in a door-way with the remains of a half bottle of cheap whisky when a middle aged man approached him.

'You look freezing, sonny. What something to warm you up?'

'Sure. What've you got?'

'Come with me to my car, I've got plenty in there, almost any-thing you could think of in fact.'

'Fine with me,' said Ricky, and he followed the man into an al-ley where a beaten up white van was parked.

'Get in the back sonny, and tell me what you want.'

'Are you my fairy godmother?' Ricky laughed.

'You could say so!' laughed the man. 'More the fairy than the godmother, though, if you get me.'

'I've nothing against fags,' said Ricky.

'That's good, because you've got to get right up against this fag good and proper if you want that hit that I see screaming out of your bonny face.'

Ricky was appalled, but equally desperate. He told me he just thought if he could do it and not think about it, he'd manage. After all, he said, much, much later, when his story all came pour-ing out, there were worse things in life than having to suck a cock for a hit. Think of Angola, or Cambodia.

'So what d'ya want me to do?'

'Suck me off, of course! And make it nice and slow, cos that's how I like it, see? I want to get my money's worth, sonny. If you make me come too quickly, you'll only get half of what I'll give you, so you take it nice and slow. And play with my balls while you're at it.'

'What are you going to give me in return?'

'I'll give you enough of what you want to get you through the next twenty-four hours. Will that do?'

'Yeah, that'll do fine.'

'Get on with it then.'

And he unzipped his trousers and took out his stinking, unwashed cock. Ricky had had plenty of sex but never with a man, and it was only his need for a line that made him bend over and take the man's foul cock in his mouth.

And that's how it started. He became well known and well liked in the gay community and could soon pick and choose among the men who wanted him. Occasionally there were even fights over him. He quickly discovered that most of the men wanted anal sex rather than blow jobs, and he could demand a high price for his beautiful young body and soon became inured to it. He said that the only good thing about it was he could insist on a quick hit first, which knocked most of the pain on the head and at least he didn't have to look the man in the face, or put his mouth anywhere near him. He tried to imagine he was far away on a beautiful tropical island and that it was happening to someone else, but often the men were drunk and violent and he was left torn and bleeding and couldn't work again until he had healed. He insisted that his tricks wore a condom and that saved him from catching AIDS. They didn't like it, but he was prepared to take a smaller hit if necessary for his protection and he was never without a few packets in his pocket. Ironic isn't it? He was killing himself with alcohol and cocaine, and yet he was worried about catching AIDS!

He lived like this for months, sometimes going back to the men's homes or flats, often amazed to discover they were married and had children. On those nights at least it was in a bed, and if he stayed over he charged double, and insisted on a bath and a good meal afterwards. He had sex against the sea wall, in the back of camper vans and in the cabs of lorries, in shop doorways and in public lavatories, in fact anywhere they damned well liked, he said, as long as got his whisky and cocaine, he didn't care any more.

His self-esteem was rock bottom and he was filled with revulsion at what he had allowed himself to become, and the more he hated himself, the more cocaine he snorted, and the more he drank. But he became careless, and was caught having sex just inside a small public park by an off-duty policeman, and ran away before the Black Maria arrived. Terrified of imprisonment, he ran across town and caught a bus back to Newcastle and spent the night cowering inside a greenhouse in an allotment, listening to police sirens wail across the city, searching for him, he thought, in his fear and paranoia. Then for three days he hid in our garden shed again, and when he couldn't hold out any longer, he slipped back to Tynemouth to make some money for a hit. But the gay community had heard about his near arrest and told him to clear off for a while, until the heat was down. No one wanted to know him, his trick had been arrested as he couldn't run fast enough, and those who were still around were extremely tense and nervous, and most had gone underground for a while. The cops had begun a clean-up of the pick-up areas in Newcastle and Tynemouth, and every night there were more arrests. It was a dangerous time, and so he came back to our house and in the late morning, when he had seen all of us leave the house for work and school, he let himself in and drank half a bottle of whisky. Then he ransacked the house for cash, taking everything from my jewellery box and emptying the girls' money boxes. He had just finished and had gone downstairs to find some food and was opening the fridge, when he heard the front door open. Tommy had been reading a report on a student the night before and had forgotten to take it with him in the morning, and had popped back at lunch time to collect it.

Ricky had drunk a huge amount of whisky on an empty stomach, and was suffering acute cocaine withdrawal, so he was half demented when he heard the front door open. Not knowing who it was, he took a claw hammer from a drawer and crept towards the kitchen door and hid behind it. Tommy heard the drawer open and close and assuming it was me, came into the kitchen to say hello. Ricky rushed at him like a mad man, and began to swing the hammer at his face. Tommy was completely taken by surprise, but caught Ricky's arm just before it fell.

'Ricky, it's me, Tommy! It's *Tommy*! What the hell are you doing?' he shouted at the top of his voice, but Ricky didn't seem to recognise Tommy, and tried to hit him with the hammer again and again, but he was so drunk he was clumsy, and Tommy managed to cover his head at every swing, until he was able to wrestle the hammer from him.

'For Christ's sake, Ricky, stop it! What's got into you?' It was clear to Tommy that Ricky could hardly see straight, and so he tried to calm him down.

'It's O.K., Ricky. Calm down, will you, for Christ's sake!' But Ricky was too out of it to hear him, and struggled to grab the hammer back. They wrestled over it for some minutes, sweat poring from their faces, before they both overbalanced and fell heavily to the floor. Tommy lost his grip on the hammer which went flying across the kitchen and crashed onto the draining board, shattering the plates and mugs that had been left to dry.

Ricky started kicking and hitting Tommy with the strength of a madman, and all Tommy could do was try to protect himself, holding his arms around his head. Terrified now that Ricky might really kill him, and using the last of his strength, Tommy managed to free his right leg and knee Ricky in the crotch as hard as he could, and with the shock and pain Ricky lost his grip and let go of Tommy. He was doubled up, howled in agony, but when he looked up and saw Tommy's cut and bleeding face and wild hair, he got up and ran out of the house. Tommy heard him shriek like a wounded animal.

Tommy lay on the floor for a while before he managed to stagger to his feet to go to the front door and look out. Of course Ricky was nowhere to be seen, so he went up to the bathroom and cleaned his face. His shirt was ripped, and he was covered in red weals which he knew would be bruises by the evening, but after he changed his shirt he suddenly felt a searing pain in his middle, and he fell to the floor and passed out. When he came round, he had no idea how long he had been unconscious, probably only a few seconds, he managed to reach the phone, and call me.

'Maisie, it's me! Where are you? Something dreadful has happened and I feel really bad, really bad. I've got a terrible pain in my tummy. Come home straight away, will you? *Please just come now!*'

'Oh God, Tommy! What's happened? Are you all right?'

'*No,* Maisie. I feel terrible! Hurry up! Just get here as quick as you can!'

'I'm only in town doing some shopping. I'm on my way!'

In a blind panic, I ran out of Sainsbury's and tore to the car, abandoning my full shopping trolley in one of the aisles. I raced home as quickly as possible, my mind racing. What could have happened? Why did Tommy have a pain in his stomach? What was he doing at home in the middle of the school day? Had he gone home because he wasn't feeling well? Had he rung the doctor? I wondered if I should call the doctor on my mobile to ask him to come immediately and meet me there, but I was shaking so much that I couldn't find my mobile in my handbag while I was driving and anyway, I would be home in a few minutes.

I had trouble getting my key in the lock; my trembling hands refused to obey my instructions. At last I opened the door and ran into the house.

'Tommy! Tommy, where are you?' I called out. A faint voice came from upstairs and I took the stairs two at a time, and ran into our bedroom. Tommy was sitting on the edge of the bed with his dressing gown wrapped around him, bent over almost double and looking ghastly. His hair was sticking up in all directions and his face was scarlet.

'*Maisie! Maisie*, this is *serious!* I know it is! I don't know what the matter is, but I feel terrible and I'm telling you, it's *serious.*'

I looked at his face and saw it was covered in weeping cuts. And then I noticed that his neck had red pressure marks which were beginning to emerge in livid bruises.

'What in God's name has happened, Tommy?' I almost shouted with shock and anxiety.

'Ricky! He was in the house and I think I surprised him. We had a bad fight. He was drunk, or high. I don't know.' Tommy paused and gripped his chest, moaning. As he started to talk again, he began rocking back and forth on the bed. 'He had a hammer. The kitchen's a mess, I'm afraid. He was trying to *kill* me, Maisie! He didn't know who I was. He was completely deranged. I think he must have kneed me in the gut, or kicked me there. Oh God! The pain. Can't talk any more.'

He struggled to his feet and hobbled to the bathroom bent over like an old man. As soon as he reached the basin he began heaving and retching, but nothing much came up. I looked at his face as I held his head, cradling his forehead in my hand and noticed that his colour had turned pasty, with nasty pink blotches.

'Call an ambulance Maisie! Call an *ambulance!*' was all he could say, as he couldn't keep still for a moment. He began to walk up and down the length of the bedroom moaning, 'Oh! Oh!' and clutching his stomach.

'I won't be a minute! Just a minute, darling!' I said, as I dashed to look in my medical book downstairs. Stomach pains, chest pains . . . I ran my finger down the page my heart thumping in my chest, my eyes hardly able to focus I was in such a panic, and read 'could be indigestion. *Often mistaken for a heart attack*. If in doubt, call a doctor immediately.'

I reached for the phone, but of course I was put through a series of menus, until at last I spoke to a doctor.

'Does he feel weak? Is he sweating?'

'I don't know, I don't know, I'll have to ask him!' I almost shouted, fear gripping my mind and freezing it. 'He's obviously in terrible pain, but I'm downstairs on the phone, and he's upstairs.'

'Then go upstairs and ask him' the doctor instructed, as if I were a stupid child, which I admit must have been how I sounded. I transferred the call to our bedroom and tore upstairs to find Tommy lying on our bed, moaning.

'Is he grey?' the doctor asked.

'Yes. He is now.'

'Where exactly is the pain coming from?' he asked the idiot child.

'Tommy, listen! Put your hand where you feel the pain.'

Tommy placed his hand on the middle of his chest, and I told the doctor.

'What type of pain is it?'

'Tommy, what sort of pain do you have? Is it a thudding pain, or stabbing, or what?'

'Stabbing,' was all he could manage to say.

'It's a stabbing pain,' I repeated down the telephone.

'Is he sweating?'

'Yes.'

'Call an ambulance immediately. Your husband is probably having a heart attack.'

Tommy couldn't stay still. He got off the bed and bent double, continued to pace the floor moaning. Ruth, I will never forget the sound he made as long as I live. I was still shaking so much I could hardly dial the emergency number, and I gabbled out our address, asking for someone to come as quickly as possible. A very calm female voice took our address, Tommy's age, date of birth, details of any medication he was on, the name of our GP, and what seemed like an endless list of irrelevant questions, until I asked her rather rudely if she'd stop asking questions that I could give the answers to later, and send us the goddamn ambulance! She assured me that an ambulance would be with us in a few minutes and that she needed to tell the paramedics all the information I had given her, so they would be prepared when they arrived. I hung up and told Tommy.

'Maisie, I'm having heart attack aren't I?'

'I think so, my darling. That's what the doctor thinks. The ambulance is on its way. Hang on darling, hang on.'

'Oh Maisie, I can't hang on for long. The pain, oh God, oh God, the pain, Maisie!'

'They'll be here any minute, darling. *Any minute*, I promise you.'

But Tommy couldn't wait. He was sweating as much water as if he were standing under a shower, and his thick towelling dressing gown was already soaked.

'Where are they? *Where are they?*' he kept asking, as he paced up and down the room, clutching his heart, and moaning. I was trying to keep calm to reduce his fear. I knew if I panicked it would be the worst possible thing for Tommy, but before I could stop him he went downstairs to wait by the front door.

'Where are they, Maisie?' he asked again, rocking his body back and forward. '*Where are they?* Ring again, and find out where they are! They should be here by now!'

I rang the emergency number again, and was passed from one person to another, who - can you believe this Ruth - told me that an ambulance hadn't been requested! Then I exploded. 'What the hell are you talking about?' I screamed down the phone. 'My husband is having a heart attack and I called an ambulance at least half an hour ago. Get one NOW!'

'O.K., dear. I'll just pop you on hold for a moment, and find out what's happening,' said a woman with a trained, calm, smooth, voice.

'Pop me on fucking *hold!*' I thought to myself. How *could* they say that to anyone waiting in an emergency? 'I'll just pop you on hold!' It was unbelievable! I would have strangled her with the telephone cord if she'd been in the room. But after a few seconds, she came back on the line.

'It's O.K., dear. We weren't sure if they were coming from the RVI or the General.' But before she could finish her sentence, I interrupted.

'I don't give *a shit* which hospital they're coming from, just get one here will you?' I yelled down the phone.

'They're on their way, dear. They'll only be a couple of minutes.'

As I hung up I saw that Tommy was no longer standing. He had tried to sit down on a chair, but had slid to the floor. He grabbed hold of my hand and asked again, 'Where *are they*, Maisie?'

'They're nearly here, darling, nearly here. Hang on Tommy, help is on its way.'

But Tommy was looking worse every second. I didn't know what to do except to soothe him with words, and wipe his brow. Within minutes of my second phone call the doorbell rang, and I ran to open it.

'Thank God! Come in, come in, he's in here' I said, as I led the two paramedics into the sitting room.

'Hello, Mr Wilton,' said one. 'We're here to help you. Now don't you worry, we'll quickly get you comfortable. But I've just got to ask you some questions first. Is that O.K.?'

Tommy nodded, but by this time he was almost beyond speech.

'Ask me,' I snapped. 'I'm his wife and I know all his details.'

'Right you are, then,' he said in a soft, Tyneside accent. 'Can you give me his date of birth?'

I told the paramedic all he needed to know without taking my eyes off Tommy for a second. He was lying on the carpet with his head resting on my lap, and I watched as he rapidly deteriorated and began sweating even more heavily. Suddenly his back arched and water started to pour out of his *eyes*, Ruth! Not as if he were crying, but actually *squirting* out of the tiny hole in the corner, and running out of his nose and mouth, and even his *ears*. It was terrifying, and quite, quite, horrible. There was a spilt second pause, and then I saw that I was losing him.

'*Do something!*' I shouted at the two paramedics. 'He's going! *He's going! Do something*, for *Christ's sake!*'

One of the paramedics ran to the ambulance returning with a defibrillator which he tore out of its Velcro packet and put over Tommy's chest. Then he looked at me, and I didn't like what I saw in his eyes. I saw fear, and doubt.

'He's going to move violently,' he explained to me. 'Just beware. You'd better move back a bit.'

'Just get *on* with it!' I shouted. Why were they wasting vital seconds explaining that Tommy might hit me when he jumped with the shock? I was so angry, and terrified. This couldn't be happening, could it? It was all so surreal. He was perfectly well and healthy, until today. He was the love of my life, my truly beloved, he couldn't be dying, he *couldn't*!

'Here goes!' said the paramedic as he shocked Tommy who, as I had been warned, jolted violently, his entire body lifting three inches off the floor before crashing down heavily. Almost immediately Tommy rose to his knees and started to fight the two paramedics who were trying to hold him down so they could insert a line in his arm to give him pain relief.

'Can you help us hold him?' one asked, wrestling with

Tommy, and I jumped to my feet and helped to pull Tommy back down to the carpet, and held his head in my lap once more.

'Tommy! Darling! You've *got to keep still* for a minute! Keep *still,* Tommy, or they can't give you pain relief!' But Tommy kept thrashing around on the floor and try as he might, the paramedic could not get a line in his arm. I was desperate.

'Tommy! Try to lie still, my darling. *Please Tommy.* Just lie still for a moment. It'll only take a moment.'

We had a few seconds when he lay still and I held his arm steady for the paramedic to insert a needle into his arm. As soon as they had succeeded and connected him to a syringe, the medication kicked in immediately and he relaxed. He was lying on the floor beside the sofa, his head in my lap, and I stroked his head, and kept telling him to stay with me.

'Stay with me, darling. Stay with me. Think of all we have to look forward to. Our beautiful retirement together. We want to watch our children marry, and be around to see our grandchildren when they come, don't we? Please don't leave me, Tommy. It'll be all right now. It's all right now, darling. They're helping you. You'll be fine, just fine, now. The worst is over. Stay with me, my darling. We've so much to look forward to, haven't we? So many good things to enjoy together.' An endless stream of inanities fell from my mouth as Tommy's head rested on my lap, his hand rising to stroke my hair, fiddling with it and twisting it in his hands as the paramedic phoned the hospital.

Ruth, I've just got to stop there. The reliving of Tommy's near-fatal heart attack is too painful for me to write in one go, and I have wept continuously the whole time I wrote. I simply can't write another word about it for the moment. I'm exhausted. I hope you understand, and now you will see why I said that there was so much other even tougher stuff to tell you before Mum died.

I'm going to bed and once I feel better, I'll continue.

With much love,

Maisie

From: Ruth Braydon <u>ruthbraydon@cedaw.com.ar</u>
Date: 8th May 2011
To: Maisie Wilton <u>maisiewilton@btinternet.com</u>

My dearest sister,

What a terrible email! I am at a complete loss for words. And certainly at a loss for the *right* words. Tommy having a serious heart attack! And *four years* ago. I am presuming – praying – hoping - that he recovered, because you neglected the most important piece of information – whether Tommy survived on or not. I am praying with all my heart that because you use the term 'near-fatal' it means that he did live through it and recover.

And my son, a rent boy. Dear God in heaven, how could these appalling things have happened? It is beyond my comprehension. I feel sick, defeated, defiled, even, by what my son has done. Was Tommy's heart attack Ricky's fault? How I wish I could have been there to hold you in my arms, and offer you comfort. I used not to be much good at comforting, but I have had a great deal of practice over the past few years and I would have liked to have tried. And I've recently discovered that a little bit of being fussed over can be very comforting.

You didn't deserve this, Maisie! Of all people, you should never have had to suffer so much. You have lived such a good life, and have given so much to others, whereas people like me, who have lived entirely for their own selfish ends, have had it easy. Life is so unfair. So utterly incomprehensible. If I had even the faintest whisper of faith, I have lost it now. There is no reason or purpose to this ravaging of lives of good people.

Oh Maisie, I am so incredibly sorry. There are no words to express my anguish for you, and my son. Thank you for telling me. I am only too aware of the pain it must have caused you having to relive it all over again as you wrote it down. How much you had to cope with, keeping bright for your children, for Tommy and then Mum.

You have my heart, dearest Maisie. I give you my heart, and all my love,

Ruth

From: Maisie Wilton maisiewilton@btinternet.com
Date: 9th May 2011
To: Ruth Braydon ruthbraydon@cedaw.com.ar

Dearest Ruth,

Thank you for your understanding. As I've had five days off, so
to speak, I now feel able to continue, as I know how anxious you
are, and it is all in the past for me.
So here goes, and I hope to cope better this time.

It seemed to take hours for Tommy to relax and for the medicine to kick-in, but eventually the paramedics went to the ambulance and returned with a stretcher. Tommy lay on the stretcher
looking as close to death as anyone I had ever seen, as I grabbed
my house keys and followed them outside and into the ambulance. It was bitterly cold and I hadn't time to get my coat. The
ambulance drove off to the hospital, its siren wailing and lights
flashing, and within minutes Tommy was violently sick. We
managed to put a paper bowl under his mouth just in time, and I
held a bottle of water in the lurching ambulance as the paramedic filled a plastic glass for him to sip. The journey took twenty
minutes to the General, but it was the roughest ride I'd ever had.
Sitting in an ambulance is like riding in a tank across very rough
terrain, and I had a hard job hanging on, making sure I was not
thrown across it as I sat sideways, my eyes never leaving my sweet-
heart, my lover, my best friend. One paramedic drove the ambulance while the other sat in the rear with Tommy and me, talking
to the hospital on his mobile the entire nightmare journey, giving Tommy's details, as we raced to the hospital.

The moment we arrived at A&E a team of medics came to the

back of the ambulance and took Tommy inside. I tried to follow them, but I was told that he would be taken straight into the recovery room, and I was not allowed to go with him.

'Sorry, dear. You'll just have to wait outside until we stabilise him. We'll be about ten minutes. But I'll let you know how we get on,' the paramedic told me.

I was left stranded and alone, outside the emergency door of the General Hospital, and I watched as the love of my life disappeared behind the swing doors. I paced the cold air, my mind racing. I didn't know what to do with myself except walk up and down, up and down, like a caged tiger, my nose running in the bitter January wind, my whole body shaking with fear and shock and cold. How had this happened, I asked myself over and over again? There was no history of bad hearts in Tommy's family, and there had been no sign of a build-up of blocked arteries. Could I have done something to prevent it? Had he been feeling ill for some time and never told me? What about the children? They were all away, and they knew nothing. What should I do? What *could* I do?

And then finally, my thoughts turned to Ricky. Tommy's heart attack had been caused by a fight with Ricky! After *all* we had done for him, the selfish, hateful boy! I could have killed him there and then with my bare hands if he had been near me. My fear and shock turned a violent somersault and transformed themselves into boiling rage towards your son. This was exactly the type of thing one read about daily, in the press. Old ladies being attacked for their pathetic pension by young drug addicts who are out of control and will do anything to get money for a hit. And this is what Ricky had become. After all the years of doing everything in my power to help him, he had almost killed my

Tommy. At last I understood the meaning of the phrase 'tough love'. I had heard it so many times at Al-Anon meetings I had attended, trying to learn how to cope with Ricky's problems, but it wasn't until that freezing night that it became crystal clear to me. It was us, or him, and I sucked dry my very last drops of compassion for Ricky, and let him go. He would have to look out for himself from now on. My job was to protect my family, and particularly my husband, from him. And I'd start by changing the locks first thing in the morning.

I continued with my agonised internal questioning until, at last, one of the paramedics came outside and told me that Tommy had been moved into intensive care, and I was allowed to go and see him. I found him in bed in a half-sitting position, his face a little less grey now, and his eyes closed. He was surrounded by medical people who were talking quietly, but urgently, among themselves, and he had a drip in his arm and up his nose, and a monitor across his chest. It was a ghastly sight, but he looked a little better, and I took strength from it.

A doctor looked up at me and nodded.

'I'm his wife,' I said lamely.

'I'll be with you in a moment. If you'd just like to wait outside the ward, please.'

I waited for twenty minutes, I think, but time had moved to an entirely different dimension ever since I first called the doctor's surgery, and minutes felt like hours, or flashed by in seconds. Eventually the doctor came out of the intensive care ward and asked me to come into a consulting room. It was tiny, and very hot and stuffy, and only large enough for two chairs and a small desk, which had been crammed against the wall. The doctor looked serious and exhausted, as if he'd been dragged from his bed after working for days without rest. He was a heart specialist, he told me, and he had been called in to take over because Tommy's condition was so serious, it was beyond the expertise of the normal medical team.

'How is he?' I asked.

'He's reasonably stable at the moment,' he replied cautiously. 'Your husband has had a major heart attack, Mrs Wilton, and the next few hours are crucial. He had another serious fibrillation in the ambulance, and so we need to monitor him very closely tonight. I'm afraid that if he has another fibrillation, we might have to operate immediately. So I have called Mr Lesser, who is a consultant cardiac surgeon, and he is coming in to examine him. If he does need an operation tonight, Mr Lesser will be on hand to carry it out.'

'Oh what shall I do?' I asked him pathetically. 'You see, all my children have been staying with friends over New Year, and none of them know what has happened.'

He looked at me with great seriousness. 'I advise you to ring them.' There was not a whisper of comfort in his voice, and with those words I heard the death bell toll. 'There's nothing more you can do tonight, Mrs Wilton, so perhaps you should go home and telephone your children.'

'I'll have my phone by my bed all night. I can't imagine I'll be able to sleep. *Promise me* you'll ring if there's the *slightest* change?' I asked him.

'Of course. I promise. But try and get some rest. He'll be closely monitored in the cardiac intensive care unit, I assure you, and if his condition changes for the worse, I will make sure that you are contacted. Just one question, Mrs Wilton. He seems to be covered in cuts and bruises. Do you know the cause?'

'My husband told me he had had a fight with our nephew, just before his heart attack. Could that have caused it?'

'I'm not sure. Perhaps. Does he want to press charges?'

'I don't know. I can't think about that at the moment. Probably not. You see, our nephew is an alcoholic and drug addict.'

'I'm sorry. As you say, we can discuss this matter in a few days.'

And that was it. I was dismissed.

I went to say goodnight to Tommy and told him I'd be back first thing in the morning with his pyjamas and wash bag, and that I was going home to ring the children.

He could barely look at me. He squeezed my hand and I kissed him gently and wished him a good night's sleep. He had a tube up his nose, at least two lines in his arms, and a monitor strapped to his chest. And on top of all this, his cut and battered face and neck were covered with purple weals and even more bruises. He looked as if he were in a horror movie. How I hated Ricky at that moment. After all we had done for him and he had nearly killed my Tommy.

'Just rest now, darling. You're in excellent hands and the worst is over, I'm sure of it' I said, trying to give him encouragement and hope before I left him.

I took a taxi home and poured myself a whisky, which I never normally drink, but I needed something strong to take the edge off my shock and dread. Tonight's the night, was all I could think, as I picked up the phone and began to track down our four children. The phone calls took a long time. I had to remain very calm and conciliatory to each one, filling them with hope, trying not to put the fear of God that I was feeling, into their young hearts. Of course I did not mention the fight with Ricky. Their reaction was what I expected; a mixture of shock and horror, and immediately afterwards, each one called a taxi and they came home in dribs and drabs throughout the course of the evening. I took some soup out of the freezer, and we sat and talked as I told, and retold, the story to each one as they arrived, white faced and frightened.

I lay awake most of the night listening to the wind howling outside, as if the very elements were echoing my feelings. Every time I closed my eyes I saw Tommy lying on the floor with water pouring from every orifice, and I had to open my eyes immediately to rid myself of the vision. At five o'clock in the morning I gave up any attempt to sleep, and crept downstairs to make a cup of tea. The house was silent, but my heart was thumping so noisily in my chest that I put on the radio very quietly, to drown out my inner turmoil. While I was waiting for the kettle to boil the radio began to play 'The Song of the Hebrew Slaves' from Verdi's opera *Nabucco*, and I stood stock still and listened with my whole being. It was Tommy's favourite piece of music, and he had told me on several occasions that he loved it so much that he would like it played at his funeral. As the music faded, I prayed that this was not a sign he had died. I hadn't cried once yet, but the music burst the dam of my heart, and I began to weep silently, and copiously. But I didn't *feel* he had gone. Perhaps that sounds odd to you, but Tommy had been my great love for over twenty-five years and I knew that if he had died, I would know, somehow. I can't explain it, but I just knew I would instantly feel his departure; we were so deeply connected to one another, body and soul.

I went back to bed and tried to read until seven, which I considered a reasonable enough hour to call the hospital, to find out how Tommy's night had been. I was put through to the Sister on the cardiac intensive care ward.

'Hello, Mrs Wilton. I've been monitoring your husband throughout the night. He's had quite a good night and slept quite well, all things considered. He is still sedated, of course. But I'm pleased to tell you that he's in a stable condition, at the moment.'

'Oh thank God! When can I come and see him?'

'Not until the consultant has seen him, if that's all right? He usually does his rounds about ten o'clock, so if you would like to visit your husband about eleven? Is that all right?'

'That's fine. I'll be there at eleven, then.'

'Goodbye. And Mrs Wilton?'

'Yes?'

'Try not to worry too much. He has had a severe heart attack, but has had an uneventful night. And Mr Lesser is one of the best, so he's in excellent hands.'

'Good. Thank you, Sister.'

The children were up by eight and in the kitchen. They looked black-eyed, as if they hadn't slept a wink either. I put the kettle on and set about making them all porridge.

'I've spoken to the Sister on Tommy's ward,' I said, trying to sound optimistic. 'She said that Tommy had had a good night with no further fibrillations, so that's very good news, isn't it?'

Four pairs of anxious eyes locked mine. I smiled a brave smile but I couldn't keep it up, so I turned my anxious face to the cupboard and took out four bowls and filled each one with hot, creamy porridge, placing a steaming bowl before each of my children. I placed the honey and sugar on the table and then a large pot of single cream from the fridge.

'Would you all like a cup of tea?' I asked, as I spooned tea leaves into the teapot.

'Maisie, Tommy's not going to die, is he? He *will* be all right now, won't he?' asked Joy. She looked ghastly, like a ghost. Shaken, and worn out with fear. I didn't know the answer, but I knew I had to keep their spirits up, as I suddenly saw in their faces as they looked up at me that, despite their outward maturity, the girls were still fragile. This kind of shock reopened old scars from their past from time to time when they had lived in constant fear and insecurity. Tommy had become the father they never had and they had grown to love him deeply. I needed to tread very carefully. I would have to give them as much hope as I dared, but at the same time prepare them for the worst.

'I hope so, darling. I really hope so. Every hour that passes gives him a better chance of recovery. But I don't know anything about heart attacks. We've never had any in the family, so I'm afraid it's all rather new to me, too.'

'But what could have caused it?' asked Sharon.

'I don't know that either, I'm afraid. But I'm going to visit him at eleven, and hope to find out more while I'm there.'

'When can we go and see him?' asked Alec. Hmm, I thought, Tommy is your role model, Alec, and you will be devastated if he dies. You've lived with us since you were tiny and never knew another father. I must not take his outward calm as a true reading of his feelings. No doubt he is churning inside as we all are.

'Shall I see how he is first, Alec?' I asked gently. 'He might not be well enough today. But you can be sure that I'll give him your love, and I promise to take you in as soon as he is on the mend.'

We ate in heavy silence, everyone lost within their own thoughts and fears. It felt as if we were sitting in a room from which all the air had been sucked out. I busied myself for the next three hours in manic activity. I gathered piles of washing and put on load after load in the washing machine, made the beds and searched the fridge and freezer for lunch. I watered all the plants, hoovered the entire house, and peeled enough potatoes to feed an army. The children huddled together on the sofa in their py-jamas and watched one episode after another of *Friends*, till I thought the canned laughter would drive me insane. At last it was time for me to go.

'Be sure to give him our love!' called Sharon, as they all came to the front door and stood together, their arms wrapped around each other as if they would fall over without support, and waved sadly as I drove away.

At the hospital I made my hurried way to the intensive care ward, searching for Tommy. A nurse stopped me and asked who I was.

'I'm Maisie Wilton. My husband, Tommy, was brought in last night after a heart attack. How is he? Where is he?'

'Oh hello, Mrs Wilton. Mr Lesser, the consultant, has just been to see him. Your husband's just over there, in that room on the left.' And she pointed to a small room in the corner of the ward. I hurried towards it without waiting to hear what Mr Lesser had said, and opened the door quietly. Tommy was ly-ing almost upright in bed, his face and neck covered in violent purple bruises and cuts. He had tubes in his arms which were ly-ing limply on top of the sheet, and a monitor ticked away above him, checking his heart rate. He looked terrible. He opened his eyes, and when he saw me he smiled weakly and tried to lift his hand in welcome, but grimaced at the pain as the needle moved in his vein.

'Hello my pet,' he whispered. 'How lovely to see you.'

'Oh my darling! How are you?' I tried to speak quietly and keep my emotions under control, but the sight of him forced unwelcome tears to my eyes.

I went to his bedside and, leaning over, kissed his beloved, unshaven cheek, discretely wiping away my tears on his pillowcase.

'I'm O.K., all things considered,' he said, trying to raise a smile.

'How was your night?'

'Pretty awful, actually.'

'Did you manage to get any sleep?'

'Not much. It's very hot and uncomfortable in here. And they kept coming in every hour to check on me, take my temperature, and look at the monitor and all that sort of thing.'

'Well at least they were keeping a close watch on you, darling. I suppose they had to.'

'Yes, I suppose so. How are you, Maisie?'

'Oh I'm *fine*, darling. Fine. Alec and all the girls came home last night, and send you all their love. Of course, they're longing to come and see you.'

'Don't talk to me about our kids, Maisie,' he said, and to my astonishment and dismay, tears began to roll down his face.

'O.K., Tommy. Please don't get upset. Everyone's *fine*. We all just want you to get better.'

'I don't think I could bear to see them, Maisie. Not just yet. Will you explain? I'm just . . . I don't know. Not up to it, I think.' And he began to cry in earnest.

'Of course, Tommy. They'll understand,' I said, thoroughly shaken by Tommy's reaction. 'They'll come in whenever you feel well enough to see them. I'll explain. Please don't let anything worry you, or upset you, darling. We all just want you to rest and recuperate.' I took his hand in mine, and stroked it as gently as I could. He had closed his eyes, but tears continued to squeeze out of them and trickle down his cheeks.

'I hear the consultant has been to see you,' I said, trying to change the subject. 'Did he seem pleased with your progress?'

'I'm not sure.'

'Well don't worry. When I go, I'll find out how they think you're getting on. I've brought your pyjamas, wash things and a couple of light books, whenever you feel you might like to read a bit. Are you tired now, darling?'

'I am, actually. But please stay with me, Maisie, for a while. Do you mind just sitting beside me, even though I don't feel like talking? I'm sorry to be such a nuisance to you.'

'My darling, you have never been, nor ever will you ever be, a nuisance! Just rest now, and *of course* I'll stay with you. Get as much rest as you can. It's the best thing for you.'

And as Tommy closed his eyes again, I took up the newspaper I had brought with me and holding his hand, I tried to read while every other second I scoured his beloved face for signs of pain or discomfort.

After an hour I left, and having said goodbye to him and promising to come back again in the afternoon, I went in search of the consultant. After half an hour he returned to the ward and suggested I join him in the tiny, hot room that I had sat in the night before.

'How is he?' I asked rather abruptly.

'He passed the night without any further fibrillations, which was a good thing, Mrs Wilton. But your husband has had a very serious heart attack which has caused substantial damage to his heart. We are unable to ascertain the extent of the damage until his heart has had a chance to recover, and that will take a few days. So for the moment we'll keep him closely monitored in intensive care, and I'll be able to give you a clearer picture of any further treatment, or operation he might need, in a few days.'

'What do you mean, an operation?' I asked in dread.

'He might need a heart bypass. The best prognosis is that he will only need a stent, but he will have to have an angiogram first, so we can see the exact extent of the damage that has occurred.'

'And when will you be able to do that?'

'As I said, until his heart has had a chance to recover from the heart attack, we don't know. At the moment he is relatively stable, and if that continues, we will be able to review the situation in a few days.'

'I see. Thank you for explaining it all to me, Mr Lesser. But he seems to be extremely upset. When I mentioned bringing in our children to see him, he started to cry.'

'Yes, that's perfectly normal after a heart attack. It makes the patient very emotional. Nothing to worry about, I assure you.'

'Really? But Tommy is never like that!'

'I'm sure. But as I've said, a heart attack changes things. But please don't worry, Mrs Wilton, he's doing quite well, so far. I was concerned that he might have to have an emergency operation last night, but he didn't, so we will continue to monitor his progress closely for the next few days. Is that all I can help you with, Mrs Wilton?'

As had happened at every visit to Mum's specialists, I was dismissed. Mr Lesser made it abundantly clear that he considered he had explained Tommy's situation as clearly as he could, and now I should go home and leave the hospital to get on with the care of my husband. So I thanked him and left, feeling empty and terribly, utterly, alone. I knew that I had to collect myself before I faced our children, and that I must keep myself bright and confident for their sakes, but it was a tough call, Ruth. So I bought a cup of coffee from the 'Friends of the Hospital' café, and made my way to Mum's to tell her what had happened and to give myself a little more time before I went home to face the children. It was a dreadful mistake.

She was wonderful, but obviously shaken. She wanted to know all the details, which I told her, naturally leaving out the part about the fight with Ricky.

'Oh darling, you poor thing!' she said. 'And poor Tommy! Whatever can have brought this on? There's no history of heart problems in his family, is there?'

'None at all Mum, so I can't think what could have caused it,' I lied. I had a strong suspicion that it had been brought on by the shock and the fight with Ricky, and every time I thought about it, it only fuelled my anger towards him.

After talking to her for some time, to my horror, she broke down and cried. 'Oh Maisie, it should have *been me!*' she cried. 'It should have *been me,* not Tommy. I'm longing to go, and he's much too young to be at risk. Oh Maisie, *it should have been me!*' And then we were both crying, holding each other as I knelt at her feet beside her armchair, my arms wrapped around her, tears rolling down our cheeks. And I felt terrible. Why had I gone to tell her so *soon?* Why had I been so *stupid,* so *infantile,* wanting comfort from my mother, when she had so much to cope with herself? I should have waited a few days, at least until Tommy had recovered a little, and we knew what the next stage would be, and after I had recovered from the initial shock. I should have gone to a friend. Why I rushed like a child to 'tell my mummy' I can't think now. Except that is just what I didn't do, think. I just went. And so after an hour, ashamed and castigating myself, as well as my overriding anxiety for Tommy, I left Mum, and drove home to my children, swearing to get a grip on my emotions and not upset anyone else unnecessarily.

Ruth, as I've said, this has been difficult to write. More later and I will not make you wait long, I promise!

With very much love,

Maisie

From: Ruth Braydon <u>ruthbraydon@cedaw.com.ar</u>
Date: 11th May 2011
To: Maisie Wilton <u>maisiewilton@btinternet.com</u>

Dearest Maisie,

Please don't feel bad about upsetting Mum. You had to have *someone* to comfort you; you must have felt so alone during this time, and also had to be brave for your children. It seems to me that you and Mum became very close over the years. You were always the closest to her, but after Mike and I left, she only had you at home, poor thing. One never imagines when one has three children that one would end up with only one on the same continent. What a strong person you have become, Maisie! I'm not at all sure I would have handled any of this nearly as well as you have done.

And I also don't want you to feel guilty in any way about your feelings of hatred towards Ricky. I would have felt just the same, and he is my son.

I await the rest once you have the strength to tell me. I'm hanging on here just for your emails.

With greatest love and admiration,

Your loving sister,

Ruth

From: Maisie Wilton <u>maisiewilton@btinternet.com</u>
Date: 13th May 2011
To: Ruth Braydon <u>ruthbraydon@cedaw.com.ar</u>

Dearest Ruth,

Thank you for your very kind words. I *do* wish you had been around while all that was going on, because I know you would have helped and supported me. You have always been strong. But you weren't, and there it is. I knew when I wrote the last few emails just how terrible it would be to read, but I had to write it all, nonetheless.

I'm sorry that I forgot to tell you that Tommy *did* survive! He is sitting beside me now as I type, going through a pile of holiday brochures. We plan to treat ourselves after all we have been through, and take a much longed-for trip to Egypt next January when Tommy turns sixty-five and retires. And we are having a great deal of fun in planning it. Tommy always says that half the fun of the holiday is in the planning, and in this case, he's right! His heart attack forced us to address our mortality, and in particular, that we cannot take life, or good health, for granted. So we are going to do all the things we have wanted to do all our lives, while we can.

But now, to continue from where I left off in my last, rather harrowing letter.

A few days after Tommy's heart attack, it seemed as if the whole world head heard of it. Barely legible cards from children at Tommy's school flooded through my letter box. So many of the children were dyspraxic, or had poor eye sight, but every one of them wanted to write to 'their' Mr Wilton. I was inundated with wonderful verses, pictures and photographs of children with Tommy, letters from parents, grandparents, siblings and teachers. We received so many bouquets of flowers that I had to ask the school to send an email to as many people as they could reach to say that although I deeply appreciated their kindness, we couldn't take any more flowers into the house. Most of them I had to send on to the General Hospital, until even the hospital couldn't cope any longer, and so I sent them to all the local nursing homes for the old people to enjoy, and so that they would not be wasted. I know I should have been grateful, but the inundation became just another burden at a very difficult time.

Tommy remained in intensive care for eight days before Mr Lesser considered his heart sufficiently recovered for it to be safe for Tommy to have an angiogram. I lived from hour to hour, jumping like a scalded cat every time the phone rang, dreading the worst. Tommy asked to see the children on his third day in hospital, but we decided that they should visit two at a time, as all four of them might be too much for him at once, and anyway there was very little space in his room, and only one chair. So every morning I would go alone while they were at work or college, and in the evening I would take two of them alternately with me.

Tommy had lost a lot of weight, and even though I brought him nice titbits from home, like smoked salmon sandwiches and cold roast chicken, I usually had to throw them away. He was exhausted and had lost his appetite. He didn't feel like reading and the nights were too noisy and active, for him to sleep much. The main problem was an old man in a bed diagonally to Tommy's door, which was always kept ajar, so he could see him and hear everything going on in the main ward.

'He's obviously got Alzheimer's, Maisie,' he told me one morning. 'He keeps asking the nurse if he can have a whisky. When she told him he couldn't, he asked for a gin and tonic instead! Last night, when the nurse refused him a whisky yet again, he turned to the poor old man in the bed next to him and asked him to go and get one for him. The old man, who probably also has dementia, dutifully got out of bed and was already half way out of the hospital on his way to the pub before the nurses tracked him down and returned him to the ward! Can you believe it? It's terribly sad as well as hilarious. The whisky drinker is very well spoken, and sounds rather like a retired Colonel, but the poor chap doesn't even seem to recognise his wife, either. I hope I don't get like that!'

On the eighth day Mr Lesser came to visit Tommy while I was sitting with him.

'Hello, Mr Wilton. I am going give you an angiogram tomorrow morning. If I find that your heart has not been as severely damaged by the heart attack as we hope, I'll be able to put in a stent at the same time. You will not need anything more than a local anaesthetic and the whole procedure will take less than an hour.'

'And if it *has* been badly damaged?' asked Tommy. His voice was tremulous and he grabbed my hand and held it tight.

'Then I'm afraid we'll have to operate and do a heart bypass. But this procedure is relatively common these days, and so please don't worry unduly.'

'If he has to have a heart bypass, will it mean a much longer recovery?' I asked.

'Naturally,' replied Mr Lesser. 'But if he only needs a stent, he can leave the next day.' He didn't exactly make me feel stupid, but his manner was entirely matter-of-fact.

'What time will you do the angiogram?' I asked.

'I usually carry them out at around eleven in the morning, after I've completed my rounds.'

'Because I want to be here, waiting, you see' I explained.

'That will be all right, if you wish to. There are some seats outside the operating theatre where you can wait. It might be quite a long wait, Mrs. Wilton, because if there is an emergency, it will of course take priority.'

After the consultant left, Tommy looked up at me with real fear in his eyes.

'I don't know if I can bear the thought of a bypass, Maisie,' he confessed.

'Try not to worry about it, darling. I'll be as close to you as I can be, and we just have to hope he can fit a stent.'

'It's going to be a very long twenty-four hours.'

'I know. And I intend to spend most of it praying and plea-bargaining with God. He owes me!'

'Any news of Ricky?' asked Tommy. 'Your mention of God owing you brought him to mind.'

'No. And I, for one, don't ever want to think of him again! I am so angry with him Tommy. He could have killed you with that hammer!'

'He jolly nearly succeeded without it, didn't he?' Tommy smiled at me and I bent over his bed and took him in my arms, as much as was possible with all his drips and tubes.

'Maisie, he can't help himself. But it's *really* time to let him go now, as I have been telling you for a long time. I know how much you want to help him, but we've done all we can for years now, and still failed. We can't do anything more.'

'It's all right Tommy, I agree with you. All I feel towards him now is an intense anger at what he did to you, of all people! I changed the locks immediately, by the way. There was no way I was going to risk his breaking in again. I've spoken to Mike and he told me that I should have taken the 'tough love' route years ago, as you have done. But he was still so young then, Tommy. But he's twenty-two now, and will have to sink or swim by himself.'

'I'm very relieved to hear you say that, Maisie. I've wanted to hear those words for a long time, but I understood your feelings of love and responsibility towards Ricky and of course, I wanted to help him too. But this time he went too far. Even so, I still can't find it in my heart to press charges against him.'

'I don't want you to think about it, Tommy. Just relax as much as you can today, and I'll be in again this evening with Joy and Alec.'

My nerves were stretched to the limit by that time - I don't mind admitting it. It was taking all my will power to put on a calm front, and I cracked that morning. I went to visit Mum as usual on my way home from hospital. My relationship with Inge had been chilly since the day I told Mum about Tommy's heart attack. In fairness to her, she thought I shouldn't have told Mum, and by the time I left that day, I knew I had made a big mistake. But she was cross with me, and I was annoyed with her, as I didn't feel it was her business to interfere, and showing her feelings only upset Mum even more. Of course Inge was only being protective of Mum, but it was just another added strain. But having forced Inge on our parents, I had to live with her. I told myself that we were extremely lucky to have someone so reliable and intelligent and that it was a great burden taken from my shoulders just knowing that she was there every day - by that time she was staying until one o'clock - but I wasn't always successful. Occasionally I would moan to Tommy who would laugh at me and point out the practicalities, which were that I simply could not look after everyone twenty four hours a day. I knew that, but at times I still found it galling. The other nagging problem was that Inge was costing us a fortune, particularly once she started to stay until lunchtime, and Tommy and I were feeling the financial strain on our resources. Dorothea's legacy had been used over the intervening years and so I decided that once Tommy was well again, I would approach Dad and ask for his help, which he had not once offered, and Inge had been with Mum for almost a year. He had not sold a single house and all we received from him in financial help was his small carer's allowance. Dad has a memory for figures like an elephant as you know, but has remained extremely selective and tight when it comes to sharing cash, even for the benefit of his own wife! So it was a relief for me when Inge went to Israel for another Kabbalah shindig, and she had already been away for a week when Dad opened the door red faced and almost hopping with rage.

'Morning, Dad. How's things?' I asked as cheerfully as I could.

'Bloody awful, Maisie. I can't do anything right, and your mother's all upset and she's still not dressed. When's that bloody Kraut/Nip woman coming back? Can't you get someone else in while she's away? I'm not doing this again, Maisie. I'm telling you. I'm over eighty myself, I'd like to remind you.'

'And may I remind *you* that my husband nearly died last week and is still in hospital?'

'Precisely! So *you* don't have to look after him! The bloody nurses are doing it for you, but you expect me to manage on my own!'

I'm telling you *verbatim* what he said, Ruth, in case you think I'm exaggerating, because what he said is beyond belief.

'You are quite incredible! Is that what you really think? That I've got off lightly because he's in hospital?' I snarled at him, not wanting Mum to overhear our heated exchange.

'Well you've got to admit that two little visits a day are a lot easier than caring for someone all day!' he snarled back.

'How *dare* you, Dad! How *dare* you make light of Tommy's heart attack like that! That's the most horrible thing you could possibly say, and that's saying something, coming from you. You disgust me.'

'Disgust you, do I, Little Miss Prissy? You've no idea what it's like! You just breeze in, have a cup of coffee, and breeze out again. And you leave her exhausted with all that chatter.'

'You absolute *pig!* Mum has waited on you hand and foot for the past fifty years and you're being poisonous because you're required to help her for a few miserable days, while her carer is on holiday. You make me sick! I'm coming every morning to help her get dressed, I bring your lunch and make it, I do your washing, and then I come every evening on my way home to collect your ironing, empty the dishwasher, get her comfortable for the evening, turn down her bed, draw the curtains and so on, all in between visits to Tommy and *before* I go home to cook dinner for my four children, who are tired, hungry and very anxious about their father.'

'He's not their bloody father, for Christ's sake. Stop your stupid pretending. It makes me sick. How could he be? He's *white.*'

'I can't bear to speak to you another second! Just get out of my way and let me go to Mum. If you're making her suffer or get *in any way* upset because of your attitude, I promise you, I'll make you pay!' I stormed past him, but stopped suddenly and turning round to face him again, I hissed, 'You can be *very, very sure* that when your time comes, I'm not looking after you. You can go into a home, or part with some of your precious hoard of gold to pay for a carer, or do whatever you damned well like, but you won't see me for dust.'

I went upstairs and helped Mum pull on her dressing gown and brushed out her hair. Then I took her downstairs and made us both a cup of coffee, but did deliberately *not* offer one to Dad. I checked she had taken her pills, and once she was comfortably seated in her armchair, with her coffee cooling beside her - I had to make small cups, only half full, and give her a straw, otherwise she shook so much that it spilled all over her- then I told her the latest news of Tommy.

'That sounds very hopeful, Maisie,' she replied. 'What do you think? Will he be able to have the stent? And what is a stent?'

'It's rather like a tiny bit of Eiffel Tower inserted into the artery. It's a piece of metal mesh that keeps the artery open and supports it, so that it never blocks again.'

'How wonderful! Isn't science miraculous? I wonder who invented it.'

'I don't know. Mr Stent? It certainly would be the best possible option, Mum. But we won't know until he's had the angiogram.'

'Please phone me as soon as you know.'

'Of course I will. I'll be just outside the operating theatre and will call you the minute he comes out.'

'Good luck, darling. I'll be praying for you all the time.'

'Thanks, Mum. You're such a rock. I love you so much.' And her eyes filled with tears.

I was at the hospital at ten o'clock the next morning and went straight in to see Tommy. He was very anxious and obviously extremely relieved to see me.

'Today's the day, Maisie!' He smiled up at me as he reached out for my hand, but I could see the naked fear in his eyes.

'Yes, not long now, darling.' But we had to wait until nearly twelve before they took him in. As Mr Lesser had warned the day before, there had been an emergency, and he had had to operate immediately before Tommy could have his angiogram.

I walked to the operating theatre beside his gurney, holding his hand all the way and waved goodbye as the doors closed behind him. Then I went to sit on one of the hard plastic chairs and opened the newspaper, but I couldn't take in a single word. I watched the clock move as slowly as a sloth, the minutes passing like hours. At last the doors opened and Tommy was wheeled out. His bed stopped beside me and as I leapt to my feet he called out, 'I've had a stent Maisie! They've put in a stent! It's O.K.! I don't have to have a bypass!' And we both burst into tears and simultaneous laughter. I hugged him on his bed and we had a few moments of pure, undiluted joy. It was wonderful. Utterly wonderful. Then I phoned Mum immediately.

An hour or more later, Mr Lesser came to see him.

'As you know, I was able to put in a single stent, and it went very smoothly, Mr Wilton. I'm sure you'll be delighted to hear that you can go home tomorrow.'

'Thank you very much, Mr Lesser,' Tommy replied, his joy and relief shining from his eyes.

'Will it be in his artery forever?' I asked.

'Yes, of course.'

'But how long will it last?'

'Oh, it should last him the rest of his life, with any luck,' he replied. 'Sometimes they need replacing, but not often. And sometimes another is required. But in your husband's case, he only needed one, and I don't imagine that he'll need another. I'm very pleased with the result.'

'And so are we!' Tommy added, laughing out loud in his relief.

'I'll see you before you go tomorrow, Mr Wilton. I will have to make out your prescription and book another appointment in six weeks. You must have at least six weeks off work, and then I'll see you again and decide if you're well enough to return to school. Oh, and no driving for six weeks, either. You're going to feel very tired for quite some time. It was a serious heart attack, as you know, so don't expect too much, too soon.'

'I'll make sure he doesn't do *anything* unnecessary,' I said.

'Good. So I'll leave you now and see you tomorrow. Goodbye.'

And no doubt he went off to perform another life-saving operation. Suddenly I loved this man.

Mr Lesser had been quite right about Tommy's recovery. He was physically and emotionally shattered. He could get up and have breakfast in his dressing gown, but that alone exhausted him, and he had to go straight back to bed for a couple of hours before he had sufficient energy to get up again to shower and shave. Then he went back to bed and had his lunch on a tray, followed by an afternoon sleep of at least two hours. But gradually his strength returned, and every day he became a little stronger.

After the first two or three weeks I could see a marked improvement in his energy level and we used the time to read and catch up on all the films we had missed. In a bizarre sort of way, it turned into a rather special time for us both. The children either came to visit him every day, or if they were unable to, they phoned him. Everyone was so relieved that the nightmare was over, and joyfully returned to their daily lives. Mum was longing to visit him, but she was housebound herself, so they chatted on the phone every few days, commiserating with each other's difficulties.

But there was no news of Ricky. I couldn't get him out of my mind. I was letting my anger eat me up and although I knew that it would poison me, I couldn't control it. Eventually I decided to ring Mike. We talked on Skype for hours one morning when Tommy had not been home very long, and was still spending most of his time in bed.

'Maisie, you've *got* to let go, and let him *go*. It's the *only* way. I've told you before. You've broken your back for the past six years trying to help him and it has made no difference. Until he's reached rock bottom, he'll continue to use and drink and there's nothing on this earth that you, or anyone, can do about it. You've got more than enough on your plate looking after Tommy and Mum. If you carry on like this, you'll be the next one to have a heart attack, and then where will you be?'

It was good sense, and I was so grateful to Mike for the time and trouble and loving concern he showed me. I didn't learn anything I didn't already know, but I had to hear it all over again. Mike promised to come over in the spring, as he knew that Mum was fading. I didn't tell him about my run-in with Dad. What would have been the point? No use in making Mike angry, and he was so far away, and there was nothing he could do about it anyway. Dad and I had avoided each other like the plague yet again since that terrible morning, but hiding it from Mum turned out to be just an added strain on me. I remembered Tommy's offer of a trip to a health farm all those years ago, which I had never taken. I promised myself that once he was back to work, I would finally take it. Did I tell you that when he was pacing the floor in acute pain he turned to me and said, 'Maisie, if anything should happen to me, I want you to know that you've been the most wonderful wife and mother?' Wasn't that incredible? And typical of him too, that even in his agony he was thinking of me, and wanted to comfort me.

I won't wait for a reply. I'll write again in a few days, because to be honest, I rather want to get back to Mum and get this all over. We have been writing to each other for such a long time now, and still I haven't arrived at Mum's death. I didn't realise when I began that there was so much ground to cover. So I'll plod on - otherwise, at this rate, *we'll* be dead before I reach the end!

With very much love,

Maisie

From: Maisie Wilton maisiewilton@btinternet.com
Date: 21st May 2011
To: Ruth Braydon ruthbraydon@cedaw.com.ar

Dearest Ruth,

I've had a few days rest from the family history, and Tommy and I have been on several beautiful walks taking advantage of the lovely early summer air. On Sunday we went to Dustanburgh Castle and had lunch in an olde worlde pub in Embleton. We've been to Holy Island, crossing the famous causeway, and even had time for a walk *and* lunch, all before the tide turned. This weekend we are planning a family outing to Alnwick Castle to see the Duchess's new garden. Alec has his own car now, as does Sharon, so they are insisting on driving us! It feels as if the good times are back again.

But to continue, and go back to four years ago. By now you had been gone for seven years and your continued silence remained a mystery to us all. We were utterly at a loss to understand why you had stayed silent, and for so long. But no one suffered as much as Ricky. His suffering was like a cancer spreading throughout his body and it had taken its hold in addiction. I couldn't accept it, Ruth, no matter how hard I practiced tough love. I feared daily for his life, and I hated you for it. I'm sorry Ruth, but I found myself less and less able to understand you as the years passed, while Ricky lurched from one crisis to the next. I know now that he might always have been an addict, but he also might *not,* had his circumstances been different. I felt strongly about Billy deserting them too, but there is something about a mother deserting her children which runs against human female programming. How *could* you have done it, Ruth? I don't think I'll ever understand. Was it really just for freedom and love? It sounds so facile, to wreck so many lives for romantic love and freedom. Nothing will reverse Tommy's heart attack, but it was his heart attack that finally saved your son. And this is how it happened.

Ricky had run from the house in a confused state of alcohol-fuelled madness. As he slammed the front door behind him, he had become aware that he had attacked Tommy, not a burglar, and he was stricken with shame and terror. Not knowing what to do, and in no fit state to go anywhere, he fell to the ground behind the hedge of the house opposite and cried his eyes out, shaking with horror at what he had done. And there he lay, peering from time to time at our house through a gap in the hedge, to see if Tommy came out, and if he was all right. He couldn't understand why Tommy had been at home in the middle of the day and expected him to leave at any moment to return to school.

What he saw first was my car screech to a halt outside, and he watched as I struggled to fit my key into the lock. Before the door slammed shut, he heard me call out 'Tommy! Tommy where are you?' and he knew that something bad must have happened to him. His anxiety grew so great that his heart began thumping wildly in his chest, and then he was violently sick. His anxiety only increased as he watched the ambulance arrive and then, less than fifteen minutes later, as Tommy was carried out of the house on a stretcher, with me following behind. Almost immediately the ambulance shot away, its lights flashing and siren wailing, and that was when he broke down completely, wailing and rocking, his spirit shattered. He had killed Tommy, he was sure of it, and he would go to prison for murder.

He told me later, much later, when he finally told me the whole truth, that this had been his turning point. He had reached rock bottom, and he knew he could not carry on a day longer drinking and taking drugs. He needed help, and he needed it immediately, and yet he was frozen to the spot, quite unable to move, to think, to do anything but wring his hands and cry. He said the fear that gripped him was so all-consuming that he was immobilised in total shock, for what seemed like hours. And then, as black night descended, he remembered St Mary's cathedral, opposite the station. He wondered how many times he had read the words 'Narcotics Anonymous Meeting' on the church notice board, as he was being taken by yet another greedy trick. And at that moment, he knew, with terrifying clarity, that this was his only hope of survival. If he wanted to live, he *had* to get there.

It took him over an hour to walk to the hall, but the exercise, and the sharp night air, forced his blood to circulate through his stiffened limbs, and although he was freezing cold and stinking of vomit, he was almost sober by the time he arrived. A meeting was already in progress, and as Ricky walked into the hall, a whole roomful of faces turned to look at him, and he couldn't bear it. He was certain they all knew he was a murderer, that they could read his guilt on his face, and the shame and agony unravelled the tenuous hold he had on himself, and he fell to the floor and began to weep again. A stunned silence had filled the hall, and then several men rose from their seats and came over to him, gently helping him to his feet, and taking him to a quiet corner.

'It's O.K., lad,' were the first words he heard. 'We've all been there. There's nothing you've done that we haven't all done before you.'

'*No!* It's much worse than you think!' Ricky wailed. 'I'm a *murderer!* I killed my uncle while I was drunk! Jesus fucking *Christ!* I *killed* him! *I know* I did!'

'What happened, sonny?' one of the voices asked. Ricky had been led to a chair and was sitting with his head in his hands; he couldn't bear to look at any of them.

'I went to their house to steal some cash for a hit. Then I drank whisky, lots of it. Then, then he came in and I thought, I don't know what the fuck I thought, that it was a burglar or something, so I took a hammer and we, we began to fight, and oh God! I must have hit him. There was blood everywhere and we fell to the ground, and then I ran out of the house, and then my aunt came, and . . . and . . . and he's gone off in an ambulance. I know I killed him. I don't know what to do. Help me. Please help me. I just want to top myself!'

'It's O.K., lad. You're safe here. We'll look after you. First things first, though. If your uncle's gone off in an ambulance, he's not dead, is he? So let's not worry about that. Most likely he's in need of some stitches, and the like. Now, let's get some food inside you, and a hot cup of tea. We've got some cheese sandwiches, I think. D'you think you could stomach one of those?'

Ricky looked up towards the gentle voice with a soft Tyneside lilt, and saw a middle-aged man looking at him, his eyes full of genuine concern above fleshy cheeks. He nodded.

'Right you are, then. Denny, will you see to it, mate, while I take the lad out of the hall to our quiet room?' And he helped Ricky to his feet, and taking his arm, led him gently away.

His name was Tony. Tony Kay, and he was a disbarred solicitor who was now a gardener for the council and who volunteered his legal expertise at the Citizens Advice Bureau. He had been in recovery for fifteen years and he became Ricky's sponsor and saviour. He took Ricky home with him that night and gave him a hot bath and some clean clothes. He lived alone and was glad of the company, he assured Ricky. The following day, Ricky told Tony everything. And Tony listened softly, never interrupting him, only occasionally getting up to make a fresh pot of tea and plates of hot buttered toast. Ricky stayed with Tony for a whole year. Tony found out what had happened to Tommy, and that Tommy's heart attack had not been caused by their fight, but from years of furring arteries.

'The doctor *assured* me that he would not have had a heart attack just from a scrap like yours. "No, absolutely *not,*" he said. It could have been anything that triggered it. He was "a walking time bomb" the doctor said, "a walking time bomb". Now lad, you must believe me,' Tony said, as Ricky shook his head in incredulity. 'If you don't believe the doctor, then where are we? Eh? Your uncle did not have a heart attack because of you, Ricky. That's the truth, plain and simple. He had a heart attack because his arteries were blocked. It's a miracle that he didn't die years ago, by the sound of things. *So it was not your fault!* O.K.?'

Around that time I went to the theatre and saw an incredibly powerful play by a brilliant British playwright called Lisa Evans. It was about three women who had suffered from very different tragedies. One woman, who was caught up in the Balkan war in the 1990's, was raped by people who had been her neighbours and members of her mixed community. She conceived a child, but she could not face rearing that child 'of forty fathers and no father' and so she murdered her baby at birth. The second woman gave birth to a Down's syndrome baby and was attacked and vilified by her mother. Of course now I know the story of our mother, I found this part extremely moving. But it was the third character, a simple 1950's Yorkshire woman who held my attention the most. She had two daughters and one afternoon they went to the local shops to buy sweets. Her eldest daughter, who was about ten, never came home. There were no sightings, no body, no scraps of clothing, nothing but a life sucking question: what had happened to her? She waited for years for her daughter to come home and her waiting and obsession almost drove the family apart. The strain on the younger daughter who had returned from the village safe and sound was terrible. In the end she begged her mother to forgive her for being the one who survived. Of course the mother put her missing daughter on a pedestal and lost all interest in life, hers or anyone else's. The play was called *Once We Were Mothers* and it spoke directly to my heart. I wept silently the whole way through and continued to weep occasionally for days afterwards. Of course, the story of the mother with the missing child was the one that affected me the most. It spoke of all the issues that surround a disappearance. The most terrible thing, it seems to me, is *not knowing*. It leaves the mind free to create horror after horror, and it is almost impossible to control these thoughts. One becomes one's very own mental torturer. For those left behind, life becomes an endless, fruitless search for meaning, overlade with dashed hopes, ripped apart and scarred by bitterness and frustrated anger. Not knowing is as bad as abandonment. And abandonment is a living death. Sometimes hope can be, too. There is freedom and release in letting go of hope, and a chance to make a fresh start. But if we hang on to hope for too long, it ceases to be a life raft, and becomes the reeds that attach themselves to our ankles and drag us under the water, to drown. But for all those lost years, I had been as incapable of giving up hope that Ricky would turn up, as he probably was that he would see you again, even though I could see that my raft was rotting and I began to feel the reeds scratching at my ankles.

But my life was not all Wagnerian tragedy; we had plenty of merry Rossini moments too. My children began to grow up and pass exams, and the girls had nestled down within our walls and less and less frequently had major outbursts or crises. These were more often than not triggered by a passing comment about their parents or their race, but those comments always hit Sharon the hardest. It must have been because she was the one who was abused and the most horribly treated and as the eldest, remembered those ugly years with greater clarity. Sadie and Joy suffered from deep-rooted fear and insecurity, but by the time they were in their teens they felt safe at last, for it seemed as if we had lived together forever. By the time Tommy had his heart attack, they had been to college and were beginning to move out and make their own lives.

One of the great joys at that time was watching your lovely daughter Jane fall head over heels in love. We first heard about Chris when she came to remove Mum's stitches from her forehead after her fall.

'Grandma, I've got something to tell you. I've met a really nice man!'

'Halleluiah! I was beginning to think I'd go to my grave without seeing you married.'

'Grandma! For goodness sake, I've only just met him!'

'Well, what's he like?'

'He's gorgeous! He's very tall, over six feet two, and has dark brown hair and hazel eyes. He's a junior doctor and is going to specialise in neurology.'

'And does this gorgeous junior doctor have a name?' Mum pulled away from Jane and looked up at her, removing her glasses and giving her one of 'Mum's looks.' You know, the quizzical, one eyebrow raised, amused but penetrating look that saw right to the heart of the matter.

'He's called Christopher Curtis, but everyone calls him Chris.'

'Or Dr Chris?'

'No. Just Chris these days.'

'And?'

'And what?'

'Is that all I'm allowed to know?'

'What else do you want to know Grandma? Wait! Don't answer me till I've taken out this last stitch. Keep very still please.'

'I have Parkinson's you know.' Mum's dry wit was still in tact.

'Yes, sorry. Sit as still as you can.'

'Ouch.'

'Sorry. Are you OK?'

'Fine, thank you, Jane. Tell me everything, I'm all ears.'

'Well, we met about a month ago on the ward. He was doing his rounds and I went with him when he came to my ward. In between talking to patients we chatted a bit and he asked me out, but it wasn't till ten days later that we both had the same evening off. He took me to Rosario's in Bridge Street. You know, the Italian restaurant, it's been there for years.'

'I remember it well. Is it still good?'

'Yes. We had a delicious meal. He's very good company and easy to talk to. He'll make a wonderful specialist because he really listens. I'm afraid not all doctors are natural listeners.'

'I know only to well to my cost. You should meet Mr Smythe, my Parkinson's specialist. About as warm and charming as a glacier. He makes you feel as if you have come to an auto-da-fé rather than his consulting room. Where does he come from, this Chris Curtis?'

'Hexham. His father is a GP and one of his brothers is also a doctor.'

'Sounds like a family epidemic!'

'It certainly does seem to go in families. In fact the medical board prefer to take students who come from a medical background because they have a good idea of what the life is like.'

'How old is he?'

'He's twenty-six. His brother is twenty-eight and he has a thirty-year-old sister, who's married and has a daughter.'

'Have you met his family yet?'

'Good heavens *no*, Grandma! It's far too soon, but he does want to take me over for lunch one weekend - but it's not easy finding a Sunday when we're both off duty. He plays violin too, and rugby. He loves foreign films and theatre and music and is *so* interesting. You'll like him, I'm sure.'

'Does that mean that I'm going to meet him?'

'Of course! You're first on my list, but I don't know when.'

'Unfortunately I'm not going anywhere, Jane, so bring him over whenever you can!'

Chris was an instant hit when we met him at last, three months after Jane first told Mum and me about him. He is one of those remarkable people who can slip into a family as effortlessly and comfortably as pulling on an old cardigan. He has laughing eyes, which I have found to be a reliable indicator of the general good nature of a person, and a quick wit, and saw a funny side to everything. He was also able to talk to anyone about anything in the most natural, relaxed, manner. He knew all about *The*

Frobisher Family, that's a popular television sitcom – do you get it in Argentina? -and talked to Sharon and Sadie about the characters and plot. He chatted just as easily to Alec about the economy, and then discussed Newcastle United's season in depth. He glided from one person to another and unerringly asked each one exactly the right question, and listened to their reply with genuine interest. It was love at first sight for all of us. By the way, did I mention that he is also extremely good looking?!

Jane had been worried that he might be shocked by her family situation because his was so stable, so she glossed over the real situation and told him that you lived in Argentina and that her father was in another relationship, and her brother was living in London. It was only when Ricky turned up again that she finally told him the whole story, and he was wonderful to her, and she said she wished she had trusted him sooner. Jane is such a beautiful young woman, and a rare catch for any lucky man, and only a month after Ricky came back into our lives, they became engaged.

After Ricky had been in recovery for three months, he came to visit me. Tony drove him over early one morning and when I opened the front door, I stood stupidly open- mouthed, not knowing what to say, nor how to react.

'Maisie, I've come to beg your forgiveness,' Ricky started. 'And in particular, Tommy's forgiveness. Is he all right now?'

'Yes, he's much, much better, thank God, and is back at school part time.'

'I've gone into recovery, Maisie. I've been clean and sober for three months today!'

He smiled a wobbly, nervous smile at me, and I looked over his shoulder at the plump middle-aged man behind him.

'May we come in?' asked the man.

'Yes, please do,' I said, feeling completely knocked off balance. I opened the door wide and they followed me into the kitchen.

'Would you like a cup of tea or coffee?' I asked.

'Coffee would be lovely, Maisie, thanks. Maisie, this is Tony Kay. He took me in the night . . . that night, you know. I've been staying with him ever since. He saved me, Maisie.' And then he burst into tears and, sobbing openly, said, 'Jesus, Maisie! I'm so sorry. I really am so sorry! I didn't mean . . .' but he couldn't finish his sentence. I looked at him, thin as a lath and bent double in anguish, and all my anger and hatred vanished like the morning mist. Ricky was back! He was clean and sober and full of genuine remorse. It was a miracle! I took him in my arms, and even though he towers over me, I held him and hugged him and told him how much I loved him and we both wept copiously. Eventually, when we had calmed down, I noticed that Tony had quietly made the coffee which he had put on the table. I waved towards the chairs and taking a large box of tissues passed them around and we all loudly blew our noses.

'Tell me everything,' I asked Ricky, and he smiled his beautiful, slightly crooked smile, and began. His story took a long time. Occasionally he had to stop speaking, becoming overwhelmed with emotion and shame, and then Tony stepped in to fill in the gaps. It was a terrible tale, the basics of which you already know. But there was great horror in the detail. Ricky had been through hell, a darker hell than I could have ever imagined, and I marvelled that he had lived through it all and survived. Oh the joy of the aunt of the prodigal nephew! My beautiful boy had been snatched from the jaws of death and returned to us. I feasted my eyes on him. I devoured his every word. I could not stop stroking his hand. I loved him again with a ferocity that astounded and shook me. I couldn't wait to tell Tommy. I knew he would forgive Ricky in an instant. He has an all-forgiving heart, a great soul.

I offered Ricky a home, but he said that three months sober was still very early days, and if I didn't mind, he'd continue to stay with Tony for the time being. He promised to come and have lunch with us at the weekend - he wanted to speak to Tommy himself, and I naturally invited Tony too. When they left it was lunchtime, but I couldn't eat a thing. I stripped down to my underwear, and vigorously vacuumed the house from top to bottom, singing loudly to Stevie Wonder with the volume turned up to maximum before I jumped into the shower. I was high on happiness and my joy was boundless, as was my energy. I could count on one hand the times in my life when I have experienced such intense grace, for that is what it was. It felt as if the grace of God had descended from heaven, just for me. And also, of course, for Ricky.

By tea time I had calmed down enough to go and tell Mum the wonderful news.

{I had learnt my lesson not to suddenly dump traumatic news on her, even such glorious news} She instantly wanted to see Ricky and I promised I would bring him over as soon as he felt he could face her. Then she said that she must meet Tony, his saviour and sponsor. After another month of sobriety had passed, I rang him and asked him if he was feeling up to it yet. Ricky and Tony had discussed it between them and decided it would be easier for Ricky if Tony went first and told her the whole story, before Ricky visited her.

'She's an extremely loving and adoring grandmother, Tony' I explained. 'Although she hadn't seen Ricky for a long time, in fact throughout his troubles. But when I eventually told her what had happened, she didn't bat an eyelid, except to say, "Why didn't you tell me years ago, Maisie? He's my grandson and I needed to know. Did you think I was too frail to take it?" And she shot me such a withering look that I could only laugh.'

'I've heard a great deal about her from Ricky,' Tony told me. 'And also about your very difficult father, whom I am curious to meet.'

'Oh, he'll be nice as pie to you, Tony. You see you're white, and English, and Anglican. And also you took on his grandson so he didn't have to bother. Dad looks after Dad.'

'When shall we go, Maisie?'

'How about teatime this afternoon? If Mum's up to it, of course.'

'Ah, the saviour of my beautiful, prodigal grandson!' Mum exclaimed, trying to get to her feet to greet Tony, but failing. Instead she fell back limply into her armchair; she looked up a little embarrassed and then, with twinkling eyes and a shrug of her shoulders, said nonchalantly, 'Forgive me. I'm not up to getting onto my feet today. You probably know that I have Parkinson's and cancer. But please sit beside me, Tony, and tell me the whole story. I have heard it from Maisie of course, but I would very much like to hear it all again from your own lips, first hand. Perhaps Maisie will make us all a cup of tea to help us with our talk, would you, darling?'

This was during the time she was finding getting dressed, and staying dressed, was becoming more and more of a chore, but that afternoon I could see that she had made a huge effort for Tony, and was dressed and groomed and looking lovely in a pale dusty pink silk shirt with pin tucks on the collar and cuffs, over grey trousers. She was wearing her single long strand of pearls and her silver hair framed her lovely face like a halo. I thought then that I should take a photograph, but I didn't have my camera with me. I regret it to this day, as she never looked so lovely, or beautifully turned out, again.

We stayed with Mum for nearly two hours and as we were leaving, she asked Tony to visit her again soon.

'You were a huge hit, as I knew you would be!' I laughed, during our drive home. 'Thank you for being so sweet to her. As you could see, she repeats herself quite a bit. She's becoming increasingly forgetful.'

'I found her a remarkable and courageous woman. And beautiful too. Now I can see where you get your own good looks, Maisie.'

'Thank you, Tony. She *is* remarkable, it's true. And also very intelligent and extremely well read. She loved talking literature to you after you had told her everything about Ricky. Literature is her passion; she studied it at university, as she probably told you.'

'I enjoyed it too. And your father was, as you said, most congenial.'

'Hmm. The old devil. He has to do more and more for Mum and I consider it extremely good for him. She's looked after him night and day all their married life and now it's his turn to do a bit for her.'

'He's just a typical product of his era, Maisie.'

'No Tony, it's far more complicated than that. Growing up was hell. He resented our every achievement because he had to leave school at fourteen to support his family after his father became ill and then died. Of course I admire that enormously, and the way he built up a very successful building company, single handed.

But he treated us very badly while we were growing up. Particularly my brother Mike. Naturally Mike wanted to go to university and had always wanted to be a doctor. But Dad refused to pay his fees and they rowed about it for a whole year while Mike took his A level exams. Mum pleaded with him, and so did Mike's tutors, and even his headmaster pleaded with Dad, but it fell on deaf ears. Dad remained obdurate. "Too many bloody doctors already," was his single response. "There are so many of them here from India and Pakistan, why should I keep my son for *six years* when we already have too many? Anyway, I don't believe in illness." It was a terrible year, Tony. Mike had to do everything for himself, but was offered a place at Manchester University, and he worked all summer to build up some savings before he went. And when he went, he left home for good, and he *never* came back. Not once. *In six whole years.* Not even for *Christmas.* He lived and worked in Manchester and as soon as he qualified, he applied for a job in Australia and was offered one immediately in a hospital in Sydney, and has lived in Australia ever since. Then, to add insult to injury, he married an African Asian and that was the final nail in the coffin for our father. But Mike always adored Mum and rang her every week while he was at university, and if he couldn't afford the phone call, he'd write a long letter instead. But still it wasn't until she had broken her hip that he came back to visit her. Now he flies over at least once a year and every other year he brings his whole family with him. But they have never met my father, and my father never mentions their names. Mike takes them over when Dad is out. Mike has never forgiven him, even though he's a highly respected psychiatrist, he says he cannot forgive all the pain and unnecessary hardship our father forced him to endure. And most of all, the loss of his family. We've talked it through many times since he started to come home, and he's very clear in his mind. He says that he doesn't forgive Dad, but he doesn't dwell on his past either. He's simply put it all behind him and created his own life and family.'

'Goodness, Maisie! I had no idea! I knew about Billy's new relationship and that your sister Ruth went to Argentina several years ago and has not contacted anyone ever since, but I had no idea about your brother Mike. How terrible for Margaret! She must have been tortured and pulled in so many different directions. Her loyalty must have been severely tested.'

'That's putting it mildly! She's the only reason I stayed in the north. Ruth and my father had a final falling out when she was seventeen, and she left home and lived in a bed-sit which she shared illegally with a friend, until they had finished university. But Ruth was born strong and determined and wasn't as greatly affected by Dad's belligerence, because she could be just as tough and belligerent herself. They are, in many ways, very alike, whereas Mike's a mixture of both our parents and I suppose I am nearly all Margaret. I was only thirteen when Ruth moved out and I felt I had to stay at home to protect my mother and look after her. Not that she needed it, but she *had* lost two of her children and was very, very sad. But Mum views Dad differently, and sees another side of him that she has always been at great pains to convey to me. She understands him in a way that no one else can. She sees something in him that he manages to hide, much to his disservice I might add, from the rest of the world, even his own family, and she really loves him. Still.'

'I see. So conflict and disappointment have touched the second generation of your family in Ricky. I wonder if family conflict is felt as an ever-increasing burden on the following generations, as an accumulated load, so to speak, or if each generation can only focus on direct, personal impact. Perhaps otherwise it would become too heavy a load for any mere mortal to endure.'

'Do you mean family karma? I actively *do not* believe in collective karma. Sufficient unto each generation.'

'Your family certainly has a complicated dynamic, Maisie. Do you ever wonder if you subconsciously *chose* to adopt half-Jamaican children? Knowing what your father's reaction would be?'

'No. *Absolutely not.* It was just fate, or timing. But timing *is* fate, isn't it?'

'I suppose it is. I love the word "kismet", don't you? It's so evocative of *Tales of the Arabian Nights* to me.'

'I agree. I grew up loving the sound of exotic names like Baghdad, Timbuktu and Kandahar that I came across in books by Ernest Brahma, Gurdjieff and, of course, Rudyard Kipling. But now those beautiful names lie in open wounds of war and their magic has been destroyed for ever. As for kismet, I think my family has had more than its fair share, wouldn't you say?'

And what do you say, Ruth, to kismet? Was it fate that brought Fernando into your life, or something much more prosaic? You have never mentioned him in your letters, nor how you met, nor what he does, or, in fact, anything at all about him. I hope you are still as much in love with him as you were ten years ago. It has to be a *huge* love to have been worth the fallout. But then Tommy and I are as much in love today as we were from the first moment we met. I suppose we have been extremely lucky. Enjoy your love, Ruth. It is the most precious treasure, and in the end, the only thing that matters.

And now, <u>finally,</u> for the happy ending! Your son, your beautiful, wonderful boy, has been clean and sober for almost four years! He has not had a *single* relapse since the fight with Tommy, and has gone from strength to strength. He looks extremely handsome these days. He always was, but he has taken up squash, and plays at least twice a week, and cycles everywhere. Consequently he is tanned, lean and fit, and the girls adore him. He has a very good job as a researcher in a pharmaceutical company, and after living with Tony for a year, felt strong enough, and confident enough, to move back into your house.

And on that extremely happy note, I will send this email. And in my next one I'll finally get to Mum's last few days and I'll also tell you all about Jane's wedding!

With lots of love,

Maisie

From: Ruth Braydon ruthbraydon@cedaw.com.ar
Date: 25th May 2011
To: Maisie Wilton maisiewilton@btinternet.com

My dearest Maisie,

What wonderful news about Ricky! I am so happy that I cry a great deal.

And what a Herculean effort you have made in telling me the full story. I am away now, but I have asked a dear friend to come to my house once a week to see if there are any emails from you. As I am dictating to her, I will have to be short.

She printed off your last two emails and I'm so glad to have them with me, because there was so much in them that I want to read over and over again. She will send this reply to you on her way home today from my house, so please continue to email as you haven't yet told me about Mum's final hours.

I cannot find the right words to express my gratitude to you for all you have done, both in looking after my son and daughter, and our mother, and also writing to me, but it is more than you can ever imagine.

And Maisie, I didn't come here just for love. Nothing could be further from the truth. It was just a bonus, that's all and it didn't last. But it doesn't matter any more. Nothing matters to me except Ricky's recovery and my daughter's happiness. Please tell them that although I left, I never stopped loving them. Not for *one single moment.*

I'm *really* looking forward to hearing about Jane's wedding. At least that will be a joyful email!

I do, and always have, loved you to bits. And Mike. Don't ever forget that, will you?

Your very loving sister,

Ruth

From: Maisie Wilton maisiewilton@btinternet.com
Date; 29th May 2011
To: Ruth Braydon ruthbraydon@cedaw.com.ar

Dearest Ruth,

When I think that we began our correspondence last November and it is almost June, I rather agree it has been a Herculean task! But although much of it has been sad or bad news, I have really enjoyed our email conversations, and getting to know you in our late 50's. It appears that we have both changed a great deal since we were young. But that's as it should be; if one doesn't learn from life there is no point to living.

If your friend is only picking up your emails once a week, I'll write another long one today which will cover Jane's wedding and Mum's death. It could be very long, so I hope you have plenty of printing ink! But once I have told you about them, I will have covered the major events in our lives here, since you went away.

It might surprise you to know that I have discovered that I am quite a feminist myself! I am not the soft, compliant woman that you remember. Not these days! We women are expected to be bright and interesting, working full time, building our careers and *also* be at home fulltime for our children and, as we know, it just isn't possible. I often think that in some ways feminism shot women in the foot. We are *expected* to have a career these days, and women who don't work are not valued. They are generally not considered to be intelligent enough to hold down a job, by both sexes. In the past the government tried to force women back to work after having children, and have even suggested removing benefits from young single mothers once their babies were three years old. And yet there aren't enough nursery places for the children to go to and current psychological studies tell us *every day* how vital it is for young children to be at home with their mothers. So the next thing our dear government decided was that perhaps mothers should stay at home *after all*, but society still does not recognise the value of those women. Communities have suffered enormously since women went out to work because those women, while their children were at school, had cared for their elderly parents and neighbours, arranged fund raising events for charities, and carried out all kinds of care that has fallen back on the state to pick up, while they work. And of course, the state can't manage, and disasters frequently occur. How can you release mental patients and ex-cons 'back into the community' when there is no longer a community, just a big, black hole? Yet being a 'housewife' is *still* demeaning. I have always felt a deep sense of satisfaction in looking after my husband and foster family, and I gave up teaching in order to be at home for them; I had to because the girls were incredibly insecure in their early years. I know it was my choice, but I do wish it held *some* value for the rest of the world. I can't tell you how often, when I've told someone I've met at a social event that I'm a housewife, and instantly all interest in me, the *person,* evaporates. The assumption being, mainly from men, that my having no paid job equates with my also having no intellect, education, interests, passions, or even *opinions* on anything at all! And if we do work, we are *also* expected to run the home and look after the children. How did men manage to swindle us so deftly, and in front of our eyes? Even the so called 'new men' of the 1980's only occasionally do any housework, washing up or child care. And the older generation of course, don't even do that. Modern men *still* live in a 'Me Tarzan, you Jane' fantasy world of chest-thumping masculinity, and consider that real men only wash the cars, mow the lawn and take 'little Freddie' to watch the local football team. Anything beyond those duties is deemed by them 'women's work'. Men rarely learn to cook and sew and clean and iron, and yet women are *expected* to know how to unplug blocked sinks and generally be all purpose handymen, cooks, teachers, nurses, cleaners, therapists, gardeners, party organisers and givers, accountants, social workers and chauffeurs, while *also* being wonderful, homemaking wives and mothers. And *on top* of this extraordinarily demanding, multitasking life, they are damned by *all* men if they are not also slim and sexy and gorgeous and under thirty, and by their children if they are not sufficiently trendy and cool. And that is called being 'a housewife'! When we were young, in the fifties, women were brought up to believe that they should be *grateful* to their men for this life of slavery, because they went out to work in order to 'support them'. At least that attitude seems to have died out. If you presented this unpaid job, which is comprised mainly of drudgery to someone from another planet, I'm convinced they would think it was a description of a life sentence of hard labour. It makes me so mad I could spit. And children are *still* brought up with the fantasy of a stay-at-home mother, supposedly endlessly and contentedly baking and sewing and *always* available. Pick up almost any children's book and tell me if I'm wrong. Particularly the early years books, those read to children at their most impressionable age. And the great irony is this: if children don't have the archetypal fantasy mother, they'll spend their whole lives searching and longing for one. There are a lot of very busy psychiatrists to prove it.

Gosh! I've rather, as my kids would say, 'gone off on one', haven't I? What a tirade! But I know *you'll* understand Ruth, as you were always a feminist and a fighter. I used to be much more compliant, but experience, it would appear, has changed that! Perhaps it is easier to be a Stepford Wife than a foster mother with a brain, but no job title. Anyway, I want to tell you all about Jane's wedding.

In late spring last year Jane and Chris were married in a lovely old stone church in Hexham. It was a perfect country wedding on a hot weekend in early May, and Jane looked exquisite in a pale cream lace dress. She wore her long blonde hair up in a chignon and had tiny diamante stars in a trail in the back of her hair which twinkled underneath her fine veil. Mum loaned Jane her diamond necklace and I thought that I'd never seen anyone so lovely, or so much in love. Ricky led Jane down the aisle. Both Mike and Tommy had offered, but I think Jane wanted Ricky by her side both as a public expression of honouring his recovery, as well as an open declaration of her love and admiration of the wonderful man he had become. They made a spectacularly glamorous couple; Ricky in a pale grey morning suit and pale blue tie, tanned and fit from sport and hill walking.

Chris is a very handsome man and he stood tall and proud beside her as they took their vows. His family were so happy; everyone loves Jane. And with good reason - she is a wonderful young woman and you would have been so proud of her, Ruth. Of course Billy had not been invited, and in any case he had been living in California for the past few years, to be near the big recording studios. But he had heard about the wedding, I don't know how, possibly through Facebook, and he had arranged for an antique carriage pulled by a pair of snow-white horses to collect them from the church and take them to the reception, which was held in a large marquee in the garden of Chris's family home. It was a very happy occasion; the only sadness for me was that Mum was unable to come, because she was too frail. But the entire wedding was filmed for her, including the reception, the receiving line and the speeches, and we watched it together whenever she wanted to, which was very often! Mike had flown over with his family and they spent a whole day with her after the wedding watching the film, and regaling her with funny stories and filling her in with the latest family gossip. Mike and Dad did a ridiculous dance of avoidance around each other at the wedding, but Sheena went up to Dad, and in her direct Australian manner, introduced herself.

'I'm your daughter-in-law Sheena,' she said. 'And I think it's high time we met.'

Dad was so shocked he took her proffered hand in a reflex motion and muttered something under his breath. We've got it on film and it's hilarious. Dad's eyes are popping out of his head and he steps backwards away from her as if Sheena is Kali, the Indian goddess of death. You can see Sheena laughing at his reaction, looking ravishing in a bright yellow sari embroidered in gold, quite unperturbed. Then she dragged him off to introduce him to Bruce and Amber.

'This nonsense has gone on far too long, Mr Campbell,' she reprimanded him.

It worked, too. At least in so far as Dad did not deliberately go out any more if he knew they were coming, or disappear immediately into his study. He will say hello these days. A small improvement, but one that came far too late, because Mike had ceased caring decades ago.

But our mother had grown progressively weak and never left the house. The lump on her breast began to grow quite rapidly and caused her discomfort and anxiety if not actual pain, and her Parkinson's was also developing, until she was unable to do anything but read and watch television. Her sleeping pattern had deteriorated too, and Dad told me that she slept most of the evening on the sofa. She liked to watch the same films over and over again, but almost as soon as they had started, she dropped off, and of course she was then unable to sleep when she went to bed.

It was around this time that she fell on to her face, forcing her glasses into her forehead. She did recover from the fall, as I have told you, but her recovery was short lived. She had more and more of what she referred to as her 'bad days', and on those days she didn't even want me to visit, she felt so tired and depressed, quite unable to talk or even listen. She found speaking on the phone exhausting and difficult, and she saved all her telephone energy to speak to Mike, who rang every two or three days from Australia.

Dad and Mum had managed so far with only Inge until lunchtime, and I took prepared meals for them to reheat, so at least I knew they were eating home-cooked food and taking in some nourishment, as they continued to boil their vegetables to a mushy pulp! Inge had been taking more time off than was convenient during 2007 as she wanted to visit Israel as much as possible, and when she wasn't visiting her friends in Jerusalem, she was attending weekend Kabbalah seminars all over the country. This meant that I seemed to be permanently on the phone to Dora at the *Dawn to Dawn 24 Hour Home Care Agency*, trying to find the perfect temporary replacement whenever Inge was away 'Kabbalahing herself', as Mum called it.

In fact Mum was getting thoroughly fed up with Inge and her Kabbalah. Inge had promised not to talk about it with Mum, but she couldn't control her enthusiasm for the subject, and Mum was far too kind and polite to tell her to shut up. The initial enthusiasm she had felt for Inge had waned, and in those days she was more irritated by her, than besotted – probably because of her increasing frailty and lack of control over her life. She was just as annoyed by Dad, but she allowed Inge to continue giving her aural wiping, some times several times a week, and still believed it was helping her. And of course, the more aural wiping sessions Mum had, the more money Inge made, and the more frequently she could afford to go to Israel, so in a way, everyone was satisfied.

After the last run-in with Dad, I couldn't allow him to take care of Mum when Inge was away. And so I searched for another carer, and found, to my tremendous relief, a mother and daughter team. Shirley ran her own care business based in Gosforth and was au fait with all the pitfalls of her profession. She was kind and gentle and softly spoken and we all loved her and her daughter Judy, to the point that we began wishing Inge would go to Israel permanently, so that we could only have either Shirley or Judy look after her. And there were no complications with Dad, either, because they were both white and British! But neither Mum nor I were ruthless enough to dismiss Inge, so we were stuck with her until one day she announced that she had received permission to live in Israel and she would be leaving as soon as she had let her house! From that day, until her death, only either Shirley or Judy cared for Mummy, and I spent as much time with her as possible. Harmony reigned for the last few months of her life and I am grateful for that whenever I remember, which is almost as often as I relive the horror of Tommy's heart attack.

I knew that Mum had had enough of life. You asked me if she gave up hope, but hope for what? Did you mean for recovery? She knew that she would not recover, so if she had hope, it was to die in her sleep in her own bed. We had talked about going to Switzerland but even at this stage of her general deterioration, she still wasn't ill enough to be accepted.

'I'm just *existing*, Maisie,' she continued to complain to me. 'Why can't I just *die*? Every night I pray that I will not wake up in the morning, and yet every morning I'm still here.'

It was increasingly hard to lift her spirits, and I felt for her deeply. She had been through so much in her life and all she wanted was to die quietly in her sleep. It is a tragedy of old age that we are unable to will ourselves to die peacefully in our own beds. Some people do, but they are rare. Old age has little to recommend it, and I often wonder when I become frail and infirm, if I will envy my dear friends who died before they were old.

Mike and Sheena had been over for two weeks during Jane's wedding. Amber, Bruce, and his new wife Kirsty, came with them, and I am so glad they did, as it was to be the last time they would ever see Mum. They only stayed a few days before they went to France and Italy afterwards together. Mike and Sheena stayed for over a week after the wedding, and visited Mum every day, much to her delight. She was thrilled to meet Kirsty, and kept teasing Amber, inquiring if she had someone special, until she confessed that she did. Apparently he's a lovely man called Craig who owns an important art gallery in Melbourne, so I think she's given up the idea of politics and might be moving there to join him. We shall see. All I'm sure about is that whatever Amber does, she'll do it with her whole heart, and be very successful.

Mike had seen with his own eyes just how frail Mum had become, so he came back again in September. As usual he stayed with me, and again we talked all day on the days she was too frail for anything longer than a half-hour visit, and we rediscovered forgotten times from our childhood which made us both weep with laughter, and did me the world of good. Mike could always make me laugh; he has quite a dry, and sometimes dark sense of humour, which I have always found extremely funny. One of the tales from our childhood I remembered took place in the garden of Grannie and Grandpa Nicholson. It was one of our rare visits to our 'posh' grandparents and we had been booted outside so they could have a formal and uninterrupted tea with our parents, a ceremony of particular agony for Dad. I think that I was only about six, so you must have been ten and Mike eight. We were bored stiff in the garden with nothing to do and when we heard the sudden wail of an ambulance siren, we began to act out a roadside accident. As usual I was the patient, Mike the doctor very much in charge, and you were the bossy nurse. While we were in the middle of our drama, an old man in the archetypal dirty mack came up to the garden fence, which was only about three feet tall, and watched us. Is this ringing any bells yet, Ruth? Anyway, he said, 'Hello, children, what are you playing?'

'Doctors and nurses!' I said, sitting up before you pushed me back to the ground.

'Do you like little animals?'

'Oh yes!' we all said.

'Because I have a tiny little mouse in my pocket. Would you like to come and stroke it?'

'Oh yes, *please!*' I squealed. And you both said 'yes' too.

'Well why don't you come over here then?' he asked. So we went up to the fence and just before Mike put his hand in his pocket, the old man warned us, 'He's had a terrible fright and lost all his hair. So just put your hand in here and stroke him very, very gently, and then he won't bite.'

So we did. One by one, me last. He smiled ever so kindly at us I remember, and then said a very pleasant goodbye and walked off down the street. The minute he'd disappeared around the corner, you and Mike burst out laughing and started to run round the garden shouting to each other, 'Do you think it was his thingy? Oh no! Could it have been? Oh how *disgusting!*' As I was only six, I ran after you asking over and over again 'What do you mean? What thingy? What was it?' But you never told me and it wasn't until I remembered when Mike was staying that I realised what had happened! Do you remember it happening? Still, we're none the worse for it, are we? He'd be locked up for years if it had happened today. Poor lonely old sod.

Mike had only been gone a month when Mum's health plummeted. Either Shirley, Judy or I stayed with her all day and after a couple of weeks, I began to sleep in my old room to cover the nights. I would arrive about six o'clock and make something for them to eat after saying goodbye to Shirley or Judy. We'd have a sandwich or something light in front of the television, Dad in his chair, Mum beside me on the sofa, and then I'd help her get undressed and into bed about nine. The evenings, like the days, were broken up into twenty minute intervals between hurried trips to the downstairs loo, not always reached in time. Some days she couldn't even talk and would end a conversation looking at me in frustration and despair and waving her shaking hands would mutter, 'Can't speak, Maisie. Sorry.' And her eyes would fill with tears, which made mine fill too, in sympathy.

She couldn't remember much either, but that was all right except for lunch, which was on her mind all morning for some reason, probably from a lifetime of having to provide it. She would ask me to put the oven on every morning while we were having coffee – and a brandy by this stage. Mum, not me!

'But Mum, it's only eleven o'clock,' I'd protest.

'Never mind, Maisie, just go and put it on will you? Judy might forget.' And so I would. What was the point in agitating her further? She was very agitated most of the time, and I was told that this was part of her Parkinson's. She couldn't sit still for a second; she moved restlessly all the time, putting her feet up on the footstool beside the sofa and almost immediately taking them down again. Then a few seconds later up they went again, and then down again. When she wasn't having restless leg syndrome, if that's what it was, she had to get up and move around. No wonder she was exhausted by the evening!

No one who looked after her trusted her out of their sight. I had bought a pair of baby alarms a year before so that she could call for help if she needed it if she were out of sight, or in a different room from Dad in the evening for example, or if she were upstairs, which was much more likely, and he was watching sport on television downstairs. When I began to stay overnight, I would take the baby alarm into my room so I could hear her during the night. Dad had moved into Mike's old room years before, so at least he could get a good night's sleep. Of course I didn't sleep terribly well because Mum would wake up many times during the night and either watch a DVD on the small television beside her bed, or listen to music. It was difficult to drown out the rousing music from *Seven Brides for Seven Brothers*, or *Gigi* and still hear her if she called, so I didn't dare lower the volume. I was becoming extremely tired and so once a week Judy would swap with me, and I'd do the day and she'd stay overnight. On my night off I would go home and crawl into my lovely double bed and sleep for twelve hours at a stretch, and still wake up tired. But I told myself that I would have the rest of my life to catch up on my sleep, and that Mum needed me *now*. The one night a week just about kept me sane during those last few weeks.

It was also a very precious time. Dad and I healed our wounds as much as we were able, in so far as we no longer avoided each other, and he even became quite tender towards me, while I tried my best to reciprocate. I thank God every day for those few weeks that I had with Mum before she died, as I felt I had time to say goodbye.

On Monday of Mum's last week, I had turned her light out and was only halfway across the passage to my room, when I heard a terrible crash. I ran to her room and found her lying on the floor.

'Mum! What happened?' I called out. 'Why did you get up again?' But she lay like a stone on the carpet and I had to go and ask Dad to come and help me lift her as gently as possible and put her into her armchair, because she refused to go back to bed. She must have hit her head on the hard dressing table chair leg, and a large violet bruise was already spreading from her ear down the left side of her neck. She looked ghastly and shuffled her body all night, agitated and in terrible pain, quite unable to sleep. Every time she moved she would moan, and hold her hand up to her neck. It was a terrible sight, Ruth. She looked extremely uncomfortable but I could not persuade her to lie down in bed, which I was sure would be better for her. I sat beside her the whole night through and all night she moved her legs up and down from the foot stool. But after this fall she could no longer move them herself, so every few moments I lifted them up for her and only a few moments later she wanted them down on the floor again. Up and down they went, up and down all night, for over eight hours, until at last light broke and morning came, and I called her doctor.

Ruth, I have to finish here. I'm shattered now, as you can imagine, but will write again as soon as I have had a good night's sleep. Till tomorrow then!

Lots of love,

Maisie

From: Maisie Wilton <u>maisiewilton@btinternet.com</u>n
Date: 30th May 2011
To: Ruth Braydon <u>ruthbraydon@cedaw.com.ar</u>

Dearest Ruth,

I slept for ten hours last night and so, feeling refreshed, will carry on to the end today because we are going to Bamburgh this evening for a week over the bank holiday weekend and half term. I just adore Bamburgh and I am so looking forward to walking along the silver sand and breathing in the sea air.

'It's Mrs Wilton. My mother, Mrs Campbell, fell in the night, and is in agony. Please can you come and see her as soon as possible? I asked.

'How did she fall?' the G.P. asked.

'I'm not sure. I've been spending the night here for the past few weeks and I had only just said goodnight to her and was walking towards my bedroom when I heard a crash. I think she must have tried to get and up to go to the loo, and fell.'

'Is she badly hurt?'

'Yes. She must have hit her head on a hard chair leg on the way down and spent the night holding her neck, and crying in pain. She has an enormous bruise all down the left side of her neck and into her shoulder, but I don't know what damage she has done.'

'I'll be over as soon as I've finished my morning clinic.'

When Judy arrived at nine o'clock she was very concerned and upset. She began to cry, and as soon as she had calmed down, she said to me, 'That's the trouble with this job. We become very fond of our patients and then we watch as they fade. I've lost so many old people I love and it's just as hard every time.' So I tried to comfort Judy and made her a cup of coffee.

'She's a particularly wonderful lady,' Judy told me later, when I eventually went downstairs to make myself some breakfast. 'A real lady, and still so beautiful. It has been an honour to know her.' I was touched to see how fond she was of our mother.

There was nothing Judy could do that morning as of course I wanted to stay beside our mother, and so I asked her if she would mind doing the ironing and prepare lunch, as Dad still had to eat. The lovely Judy complied; nothing was ever too much trouble for her.

At twelve the doctor arrived and went straight upstairs to visit Mum.

'Mrs Campbell, I really ought to call an ambulance to take your mother to hospital for an X-ray. It's very difficult to know how to treat her if I don't know what damage she did when she fell,' she said, after having inspected Mum's violently bruised neck.

Mum looked up at me in horror and cried out like child, begging me to help her.

'*No!* No Maisie! Tell her I can't go to hospital again! *Tell* her, *please!*'

The doctor looked at me with her eyebrows raised in question.

'The last time she went she hated it,' I explained.

'*Yes! Yes!*' Mum cried in agreement.

'She couldn't wait to leave and I don't think she'd manage the journey in an ambulance. They're very rough.'

'Well, I don't know what else to suggest,' said the doctor, looking extremely concerned.

'Can't you give her something for the pain? You can see she's in agony,' I begged. I was almost as agitated as Mum by this stage. Her pain was obviously worse – she was almost unconscious now, rocking and moaning. It was quite awful, Ruth.

'I'll give her a morphine tablet and an antispasmodic pill and see if that releases the pain in her neck,' the doctor said. 'I'll come back again this evening to see how she is.' She wrote out a prescription and I sent Dad straight to the chemist.

I tried the whole day to get her into bed, but she refused. She had a large armchair beside her bed which could move into a reclining position and had a foot rest, and she didn't want to leave it. She couldn't manage to walk to her loo unaided, and Judy and I had to almost carry her there and lift her up again, once she had been.

'I think she's going to need a commode,' Judy told me at lunchtime. 'Do you think you'd be able to buy one?'

'Good idea. But I've no idea where to find one.'

'We usually borrow them from the Red Cross,' Judy said. But when I called the Red Cross I was told that all their commodes were out on loan.

'I'll buy one,' I told Judy. 'We can manage lifting her together during the day, but what will happen tonight when I'm alone? I'm not sure if I can support her by myself, but if I only have to lift her out of the chair and on to a commode, perhaps that will be possible. What do you think?'

'Even with a commode it might be very difficult. Would your father be able to help?'

'God forbid! Mum would hate that and Dad's utterly useless at anything to do with caring, as you know.'

'Maisie, please don't take this the wrong way, but it might be time to call Marie Curie.'

'What? Already? But she could live for ages yet!'

Judy looked at me with her large, soft brown eyes, and smiled gently. I knew that she had been through the death process more times than she would care to remember and she knew the signs. I had to face reality. I had to face it at that moment. My mother - sorry, our mother - was in agony, and I needed to do whatever was necessary to ease her pain and make her comfortable.

'I see. Thank you. I'll wait until the doctor comes back tonight and see what she has to say.' And I belted out of the front door and went to buy a commode.

When the doctor came back in the evening, Mum was no better.

'She's had a terrible day,' I told the doctor downstairs in the sitting room. 'She hasn't been able to swallow the pills you prescribed her and is in agony, as you can see. What can we do? I can't bear to see her like this. She's unable to eat or drink anything. There must be some kind of pain relief you can give her that works.'

'I think you should call Marie Curie,' the doctor told me.

'Judy thought it was time, too, as I'm worried that I won't be able to lift her on to the commode by myself.'

'Just as long as you realise that once she starts taking morphine it will be the end.'

A pause fell as I absorbed what she said. Anything was better than watching our mother in agony. And she wanted to die, I kept repeating silently to myself. And had done for a long time. But not like this! But there was no choice.

'OK. Please use the phone and give them a ring. I'll tell Dad what's happening while you do.'

Dad was upstairs in his study with the door firmly closed.

'Dad, the doctor is here and it doesn't look good for Mum. She thinks Mum needs to go on morphine. If she does, and it seems that this is the only option as she is no longer able to swallow her pills, it will mean that she'll never recover. I've told the doctor to call Marie Curie and ask if someone can come tonight.'

'Whatever you think best, Maisie,' he said, turning from his chair to look at me, his eyes filled with tears. I could see he had been crying and that he hadn't wanted me to notice, so I didn't comment.

'She's not had much quality of life recently, Dad. It's probably the kindest thing. And anything to relieve her from her pain has to be good, doesn't it?'

'Is there anything I can do, Maisie?' he asked, rather like a lost child.

'Not at the moment, Dad. But if you can look after yourself while we organise everything, it would be a great help. Have you had anything to eat since lunch?'

'I'm not sure. Would you like me to make you something, Maisie?'

Now that brought a smile to my face! A first! Dad offering to make supper.

'A sandwich of some kind would be very welcome, Dad. Can you manage that?'

'I'll do my best. What would you like?'

'Oh, anything. Whatever you're having, make one for me too.'

And I think for the first time in his married life, Dad entered the kitchen and made us both a cheese and tomato sandwich and a cup of tea. And it was very nice.

At eight o'clock the doorbell rang. I went to answer it and saw a very large black woman standing outside with an equally large medical bag.

'Hello. I'm Jasmine, from Marie Curie. Doctor Paynton called me earlier this evening. I think you are expecting me?'

'We are! And I can't tell you how glad I am to see you.'

I took Jasmine straight upstairs, and she said hello to Mum.

'I'm going to make you nice and comfortable, Mrs Campbell, so don't you worry now. You just relax while I get your meds sorted out. It'll take me a few minutes and then I'll be able to give you an injection that will take away that horrible pain. All right? That's quite a bruise you've got there,' she said as she tutted in sympathy, leaning her massive body over my mother.

Dad hadn't met Jasmine yet. Too bad, I thought as I imagined his horror at having a fifteen stone Nigerian in his house! Jasmine had a wonderful manner and a soft, lilting singsong accent to her voice, which was sweet and low. She had three children and had worked for Marie Curie for many years. All this I learned as she opened her medical box and began to check the medication inside. Every single needle and syringe had to be crosschecked to make sure it was there and hadn't been opened or tampered with in any way, and then ticked off once it had been used or administered. I had no idea it was all such a palaver and watched Jasmine in fascination. She had even brought her own sharps bin to throw away used needles and other sharp implements. While her vast arse was pointing up to the sky as she knelt on Mum's bedroom carpet scrutinising her lists, Dad came into the room to see what was going on. Jasmine heard him and turned around, her midnight-coloured moon face beaming at him in greeting.

'Hello. I suppose you must be this lovely lady's husband?' she asked, which gave Dad a few precious seconds to catch his breath. 'I'm Jasmine, the Marie Curie nurse. I'm just about to give your wife an injection to make her comfortable, so please don't worry about her dear, she'll be asleep very soon.'

'Thank you for coming,' he replied. 'We're so relieved you're here, aren't we Maisie?'

This was such an astonishing reaction from Dad that I gaped at him open mouthed, quite unable to reply.

'Would you like a drink of anything?' he offered, and all I could think of at the time was how much I wished you and Mike had been there to witness it.

'No, dear, thank you. I need to sort out the medicines first. Perhaps a little later a cup of tea would be very nice.' And as she returned to her paperwork on the floor, her bottom rose to the ceiling once more, and Dad retreated in haste.

Jasmine gave Mum an injection and then said 'Now let's get you into bed, dear.'

'I tried all last night and all of today to get her into bed, but she simply refuses to lie down,' I hissed across the room to Jasmine, as our mother sat up very slowly and put her feet on the floor. To my utter astonishment and indignation, she allowed Jasmine to lead her to her bed and settle her under the sheets.

'That's better, Mrs Campbell, isn't it?' Jasmine cooed as I muttered, 'Well, you old devil' under my breath.

'You look like you could do with some sleep, Maisie,' Jasmine remarked, turning her kind and concerned face to me.

'Actually, I *am* very tired. We were up all last night, my mother and I, after her fall about 11pm.'

'Well, I'm here till eight in the morning, so why don't you take yourself to bed and get some well earned rest?' she asked me.

For the first time in weeks, I unplugged the baby alarm and slept soundly.

On Wednesday morning as soon as I woke, I rang Mike and told him everything.

'I'm really sorry Mike, but I think you should come as quickly as you can. They're going to put her on a morphine syringe driver this evening and you know what that means.'

'I'll be on the next plane, pet' he said. And hearing the Tyneside endearment made my heart lurch as it had always been Tommy who had called me 'pet'. After I had phoned Mike, I went to Dad and told him that I thought we should call everyone in the family and let them know what had happened, and how Mum was. He agreed, and between us we managed to speak to most of them before Shirley arrived at nine o'clock. And now I must confess that it never occurred to me to write to you before she died. I was so immersed in the immediate care that it never crossed my mind. It was only after she died that I realised what I had done and so I wrote as soon as I had time.

At lunchtime the doctor came back and wrote out another prescription for the Marie Curie nurses.

'They'll come every morning and evening to check her medication now that I have written a full prescription for what she needs,' Dr Paynton told me. 'They'll also check the syringe driver twice a day and make sure it's working properly. Please don't hesitate to call me if there is any change.' And she rushed out of the house to her next appointment.

Mum came round for a short period after lunch on Wednesday. As I entered her room to take over from Shirley, she opened her lovely blue eyes and smiled at me. I sat beside her bed and stroked her arm, taking her hand in mine.

'How are you, darling Mum?' I asked. 'How's the pain? Any better?'

'A little, Maisie. Did I hear you talking to Mike on the phone earlier, or was I dreaming? Is he coming over again?' I nodded. 'How I wish I could see Ruth once more. You know, I don't think she ever knew how much I loved her. She was always cross with me for not standing up to Douglas enough. She thought I was weak. She's a wonderful woman, Maisie, but she had her troubles. I would dearly love to see her again to tell her I have always loved her, even though she didn't think so. And I've never stopped missing her. Not for <u>one single day</u>.' Tears were running down her face as she spoke, and down mine too. So now at least you know that she thought of you all her life and never ceased to love you and miss you, Ruth. Those were her last words, and I'm sure they are exactly as she said them, and they were all about you.

Mum slept until late afternoon when she was fitted up with a syringe driver. I sat by her bedside and read for hours, not able to concentrate much, occasionally getting up for yet another cup of tea and to see if Dad was all right. He hadn't felt like playing golf, he told me. He preferred to be at home, he said, 'in case there's any change,' and we both knew that he didn't want to be on the golf course when she died.

Jasmine came again at eight o'clock and I sat downstairs with Dad as he watched Arsenal play Chelsea in the FA Cup. I never liked football much, but was pleased to keep him company. He looked exhausted and frail and overnight he had lost all his vim and vigour and suddenly seemed small, as if he had shrunk while I sat with Mum. He'd changed, and although you'd say that he had left it far too late, it's never too late till the end, is it?

On Thursday morning Mike arrived. He stayed with Mum most of the day, taking short trips to the kitchen when my children came to visit her, and began talking to Dad. The nearness to death of the woman they had both loved and adored all their lives helped to bring them together a little, and Dad apologised to Mike for all the past hurt.

'I didn't know the way I acted was wrong, Mike,' he explained. 'It was only what I thought was right at the time,' he added lamely, looking up at Mike, his eyes brimming with tears. 'And now it's too late, son. It's all far too late. When I think of the pain it caused your mother all those years, I can't bear it.'

Mike went up to Dad and took him in his arms and hugged him. They stood together for a few moments, Mike told me later, whispering the miracle of Dad's confession across Mum's bed.

'It was a complete role reversal, Maisie. He's such a sad old man now. But I hope he'll be able to forgive himself, for his sake. Sheena wanted me to talk to him years ago, but I wouldn't let her. I'm just as stubborn as the old man I'm afraid. She was right, of course. She certainly took the bull by the horns at Jane's wedding, didn't she? She's an amazing woman.'

On Friday Dr Paynton came again after her morning surgery. As she was leaving, she turned to Mike and me and said, 'I'm amazed that having been on morphine for two days that your mother is still here. Is she waiting for something?'

Mike and I looked at each other and we knew that we were both thinking of you, Ruth.

'We have a sister who we think is living in Argentina,' I said. 'But we haven't seen her for ten years. We're not even sure if she is still alive, and she has never replied from the only address we have ever had for her. If Mum's waiting for anyone, it would be Ruth.'

'What a pity,' said Dr Paynton as she opened the front door. 'What a terrible pity.'

Mum lasted another two whole days. She had been on morphine since six o'clock on Wednesday evening and lived through Thursday, Friday and Saturday. On Sunday morning two Marie Curie nurses came to check her medication.

'We need to turn her so she doesn't get bed sores,' one of them told me. 'If you wouldn't mind leaving us for a little while, we'll give her a wash and call you when we have finished.'

'But please call us if there is *any* change?' I asked. 'We'll only be sitting downstairs.'

'Of course we will,' she said, as she shut the door firmly, but kindly, behind me.

We had been in the sitting room for less than ten minutes when the nurse called down to us.

'Come quickly, she's going!'

Mike and I tore upstairs and went into her room, but we were too late, she had gone. By the time Dad arrived, we were sure.

'Will you leave us for a while please?' I asked, tears streaming silently down my shattered face.

'Of course. We'll wait downstairs. You can come and find us when you're ready. There's no hurry. No hurry at all.'

She lay on the bed, looking so peaceful and relaxed. Mike, Dad and I stood at the bottom of her bed, and gazed at her in love and loss. All her lines had miraculously smoothed away, and she looked really, really beautiful.

'Fly to the light!' I told her in my mind. 'Forget all about us and this mad, bad, crazy, beautiful world. Be free from your worn-out body. Fly with wings of the angel you have been all your life, and be free. Be free at last, my darling, beloved mother.'

So now you know it all, Ruth. I have done my best in my rather inept way to tell you what has happened in the intervening years since you went away. I hope you have been happy, Ruth. Life is but a brief passing and we should be duty bound from birth to savour every day. I try my best to follow my own advice, but I often shudder when I think of all the time I have wasted, of the missed opportunities, the kindnesses left undone, the soft word unspoken. Hindsight is a great teacher and it is true that youth is wasted on the young.

With all my love, dearest sister,

Maisie

To: Ruth Braydon <u>ruthbraydon@cedaw.com.ar</u>
Date: 5thth June 2011
From: Maisie Wilton <u>maisiewilton@btinternet.com</u>

Dearest Ruthie,

I haven't heard from you since your last email sent on 25th May.
I trust that you received my last two? They were both extremely
long, but at last you have the complete story. Are you still away?
I thought your friend was going to pick up your emails for you
and write your reply. I find I have become accustomed to receiving your frequent emails and am missing the contact enormously.
I do hope that I haven't upset you too much with my remarks and
opinions. I didn't mean to be harsh, Ruth, but we were trying our
best to be honest and open with each other, weren't we? Perhaps
honesty given so directly is not always wise, or worth the hurt it
can cause.

I expect you will wonder if I had given in and were looking
after Dad since Mum died. I have arranged a daily to come for
two hours in the morning from Monday to Friday, and I telephone him a couple of times a week, just to check he is still alive.
And he comes for Sunday lunch about twice a month, which I
do for Mum's sake, because I know she would not have wanted
him to have been completely abandoned, but that's about it. He
is still in remarkably good health for 86, and continues to play
golf every day, weather permitting, which is probably what keeps
him going. But he's a lonely shell of a man now, Ruth, and at long
last has lost the power to frighten or control me. He's become
just a rather pathetic, sad old man. We are only feathers in the
wind.

But most importantly, I have two pieces of *wonderful news!* The first is that you are to be a grandmother! Jane is expecting a baby in the autumn, and both she and Chris are like the cat with the cream. And the second glorious piece of news is that Ricky is going to be married in December! He met a lovely girl called Iona Luscombe a couple of years ago, who has conquered anorexia, and who is very creative and particularly clever with her hands. She has her own boutique in the centre of Newcastle and can hardly keep up with her orders from rock stars and footballer's wives. They make a stunning couple, as Iona is a pale, wheat blonde, and Ricky is so dark; but what makes them so remarkable and deeply attractive to all who meet them is that their real beauty shines from *within.*

Bearing in mind the baby will be born before Ricky's winter wedding, I wonder if you might be tempted to come too. I'm sure he will be glad to see you and we can all make our peace, maybe even including Dad! What do you think? Everyone is coming, Mike and his whole family, and Jane insists she will bring her new baby! They intend to call him Charles, if it is a boy, and Isabelle, if it is a girl. They bought a house in Ponteland just before they married, and Ricky and Iona are living in your house. Ricky moved back in after having lived with Tony for nearly a year, as I think I have already I told you. I will never be able to thank that man enough for his goodness. If there are real saints in this world, then he, most certainly, is one of them.

Please come, Ruth. I know nothing of your life in Argentina, but if it is a question of money, I will more than gladly send you the airfare. And bring Fernando too! He is part of our expanding family and I'm sure everyone would be pleased to meet him at last.

If I have upset you, please try to forgive me. I am so sorry if this is the case. And write soon. I miss you and your letters, Ruth, so please don't punish me with your silence.

With all my love,

Maisie

Oh, I forgot something else that is really lovely! Ricky has asked Tommy to be his best man!

Epilogue

All shall be well
And all shall be well,
And all manner of things shall be well.

Julian of Norwich, 1342–1416

79 Avenida Córdoba

4 Piso G

Buenos Aires 5008

Argentina

19th June 2011

Dear Señora Wilton,

I am extremely sorry to inform you that your sister, Señora Ruth Braydon, died peacefully in her sleep on the evening of 16th June 2011. She had been in a coma for three days. Señora Braydon had been in the care of the Sisters of Santa Ángela in their hospice just outside Buenos Aires for several weeks prior to her death. I enclose a letter from Sister Maria who was with her when she died, and cared for her during her stay at the hospice. Please allow me to assure you that everything was done to keep her as free from pain as possible, and that she received the best care and medical attention to the end. Please accept my deepest condolences.

I was instructed by your sister, the late Señora Ruth Braydon, to draw up her last will and testament and deal with her estate. Señora Braydon named you as her next of kin. I enclose a copy of her will which she dictated to me from her bed while she was still of sound mind, in the presence of two Sisters. I have sent both the original copy and an English translation. It was a simple, uncomplicated will, and I trust you will find everything in order.

I also enclose a final, brief letter from your sister which she whispered from her bed to a friend, a few days before her death.

If I can be of any further assistance to you, please do not hesitate to contact me at my office. The telephone number is on the letter heading.

With my deepest sympathy to you and your family.

Yours sincerely,

Edgardo Cortez

Hospice of the Sisters of Santa Ángela
Calle Adriana
Buenos Aires
11th June 2011

My beloved little sister,

You are the real lion. It was me who was the lamb.
God bless you.

Ruth

The Last Will and Testament of Ruth Margaret Braydon

I, Ruth Margaret Braydon, am of sound mind.

I leave my entire estate to be divided equally between my two children, Jane Elizabeth Curtis and Richard James Braydon in its entirety, save £10,000 which is a gift for my sister, Maisie Anne Wilton, specifically for their holiday in Egypt and a trip down the Nile. This gift is a small gesture of thanks to her, and her husband Tommy, for all the care they have given my son, my mother, and my daughter.

I do not presume my children to forgive me, but perhaps to understand, at last. I never expected to live longer than a year.

My few belongings in Argentina, I bequeath to the Hospice of the Sisters of Santa Ángela.

Ruth Margaret Braydon
15th April 2011

Dear Señora Wilton,

I am Sister María, and I am having the greatest honor to care for your sister, Señora Braydon, while she spending her last weeks at our hospice.

I want to write to you to tell you of her last weeks and days. But please be excusing of my English, it is weak and very littles. I am hope you will be understanding of it.

Your sister was a wunderful and brave woman, señora. She fill our lives with joys every days, and never complaning of no pains, although she suffered some much. She is always smiling and try to cheer the other patients, while she could still be leaving from her beds.

She has brest canser for long times, maybe ten years. First she has one brest taken away, but he comes back again. The doctor he wants her to have the chemo therapies, but she refuses. He begs. She refuses. Then he comes back again to the other brest. The doctor wants to take the other brest. She refuses. She says to him she is happi to die when it is her times. This is happening for many years, but she always is strong and so kind. She was not alones, señora. You must not think she alones. Her friends come all the day to visit her. Many friends, many. Good peoples. But never no husband. All the Sisters we very muches surprises she having no mans in her lifes. She such a beautiful and kind womans.

But <u>most importants,</u> she wants to know you, that she reads every letters you sending. She is so very happies with theses letters. She was <u>very happies</u> to be coming grandmothers. She cries and cries when she reads about her son, his wells again, and his marriage. This news is making her fulls of great peaces and joys. She dies happi, señora. Really, really, she dies very happi. She says to me, 'Now I am going to see my mothers again. I am going to asking her forgiveness.'

She is braves and very especial, señora. She dies in her sleep and I am with her all the times. You has lucky to have such a sister. And shes loving you very muches. All her family, she is loving them so very very muches.

God blessing you, señora. And all your familys.

Sister María

Acknowledgements

My heartfelt thanks must go first to my wonderful agent, Diane Banks, without whose faith in me and unflagging encouragement, I would have crumbled and lost all hope.

And to my friend Lisa Evans, award winning playwright, for the right to describe her play 'Once We Were Mothers' published by Oberon ISBN/HSIN London 2004.

My thanks also go to Felix Posen for explaining the real Kabbalah to me, and to my lifelong friend, Gay Schoene, who read the manuscript several times and helped enormously with the editing.

And last, but by no means least, to my beloved Johnnie and my children who kept me laughing when I needed it most.

Every hour, someone in the UK is told they have Parkinson's. Because we're here, no one has to face Parkinson's alone. Parkinson's is a progressive neurological condition. People can have a tremor or stiffness that makes everyday life difficult. Simple things like moving around, smiling, eating, getting dressed or picking up and playing with children can become impossible because of the devastating symptoms. Around 127,000 have Parkinson's in the UK alone.

We bring people with Parkinson's, their carers and families together via our network of local groups, website and free confidential helpline. Specialist nurses, our supporters and staff provide information and training on every aspect of Parkinson's.

As the UK's Parkinson's support and research charity we're leading the work to find a cure, and we're closer than ever. We also campaign to change attitudes and demand better services.

Our work is totally dependent on donations. Help us to find a cure and improve life for everyone affected by Parkinson's.

Ways to help us raise vital funds include:

Signing up for a new mobile phone deal with Parkinson's UK. We get 45% of all handset and call profits. Call 020 3476 2626 or go to www.parkinsons.org.uk/shop.

Becoming a regular giver via Direct Debit or give online

Supporting our fundraising efforts, like the Marathon or special events

If you or a family member or friend have Parkinson's, we are here to help.

Contact Parkinson's UK:

Free* confidential helpline 0808 800 0303

Text Relay 18001 0808 800 0303

Monday to Friday 9am–8pm,

Saturday 10am–2pm. Interpreting available.

*calls are free from UK landlines and most mobile networks.

www.parkinsons.org.uk/supportnetworks

hello@parkinsons.org.uk

Parkinson's UK, August 2012. Parkinson's UK is the operating name of the Parkinson's Disease Society of the United Kingdom. A charity registered in England and Wales (258197) and in Scotland (SC037554).

Lightning Source UK Ltd.
Milton Keynes UK
UKOW05f1847310713

214699UK00004B/337/P